FERTILITY
· FARMING ·

FERTILITY
· FARMING ·

Newman Turner

With a new foreword by Allan Nation

Acres U.S.A.
Austin, TX

Fertility Farming

Acres U.S.A.
P.O. Box 91299
Austin, Texas 78709 U.S.A.
(512) 892-4400 • fax (512) 892-4448
info@acresusa.com • www.acresusa.com

Printed in the United States of America

Publisher's Cataloging-in-Publication

Turner, Newman, 1913-1964
Fertility farming / Newman Turner. Austin, TX, ACRES U.S.A., 2009
    Reprint. Originally published: London: Faber and Faber Limited, 1951.
    xxiv, 248 pp., 23 cm.
    Includes Index
    Includes Bibliography
    Incudes Illustrations
    ISBN 978-1-60173-009-1 (trade)

1. Organic farming. 2. Alternative agriculture. 3. Sustainable agriculture. 4. Agricultural ecology. 5. Organic fertilizers. I. Turner, Newman, 1913-1964 II. Title.

S455.T87 2009   630.2

A Note from the Publisher . . .

It is with particular pride that we make the classic writings of Newman Turner on grass farming and natural health for cattle available to a new generation of organic farmers and graziers. A particularly sad note in our modern era of instantaneous digital information retrieval is the tendency to ignore older works. University librarians shake their heads in dismay as they note that students and researchers tend to delve into digital archives — many dating no further back than the 1990s — and scoff at any suggestion of entering the library stacks and dusting off vintage books.

Priceless insight can be found in the herd research of Randleigh Farm, the soils research of Professor William Albrecht, the traditional farming systems observations of F.H. King, or the pioneering writings of Sir Albert Howard, Lady Eve Balfour, André Voisin, Friend Sykes, Louis Bromfield, J.I. Rodale and others. Students of these great farmer-scientists, and others, quickly discern a level of sophistication still unparalleled by our modern-era reductionist scientists.

Most of the writings of these organic method pioneers were born during the beginning of the chemical era of agriculture. There was a fork in the road then, either toward sophisticated, diversified natural farming systems or chemical-based factory-style agriculture. History has recorded the fallout of the poor choice made back then in the statistics of depleted soils, poor crop quality, epidemic cancer and degenerative disease, and crippled farm economies.

Increasingly farmers and consumers are returning to healthier forms of food and farming. And the visionaries who stood firm at that earlier fork in the road still stand waiting to point the way to a new future.

In republishing Turner's writings, we've fought the temptation to modernize, Americanize, or heavily update these classic works. Obviously, currencies and their values change over a half-century. There are a few inputs and technologies that subsequent study have deemed inappropriate. And North American readers will have to pick up a few words of vocabulary as they translate from British English to American English. We present these books as they were published in the 1950s with only the slightest of annotation. A discerning reader who takes these books for what they are will walk away with a new understanding of the power and sophistication of the organic method and the beauty of farming in harmony with nature. And that reader will find lasting inspiration in Turner's love of land and beast and his plucky attitude toward the conventional wisdom of his day.

A special word of thanks must go to the sons of Newman Turner — Adam Newman Turner, Giles Newman Turner and Roger Newman Turner — for their trust in our stewardship of their father's written legacy and assistance in bringing these works back into reach of readers everywhere. The late American organic pioneer Bargyla Rateaver published editions of some of these works in the 1970s, which, like the originals, are now out of print. Like Newman Turner, she was clearly ahead of her time.

E.M. Forster wrote, "I suggest that the only books that influence us are those for which we are ready, and which have gone a little further down our particular path than we have yet got ourselves." Perhaps it is fitting that Newman Turner's farming and pasturing methods and insights into herd health are unveiled again today — after hiding in plain sight for these past decades — as interest in his brand of farming is at groundswell level. Untold numbers of new grass farmers will benefit from standing on this great's shoulders and learning anew from this simple farmer-scientist who has "gone a little further down our particular path than we have yet got ourselves."

Read, enjoy, and learn from the experiences and wisdom of fellow grass farmer Newman Turner.

October 2008

FRED C. WALTERS
AUSTIN, TEXAS

Foreword

It appears that every 60 years or so agriculture has to go back and relearn its basic truths. I was struck in reading *Fertility Farming* how many of the issues we are discussing today in alternative agriculture were covered in this 60-year-old book.

Some of these are:
- That confinement animal feeding is detrimental to the fertility of the soil.
- That both labor and capital requirements are minimized by letting the animal direct-graze the crop rather than harvest and feed it with a machine.
- That the creation of a forage sequence of perennial and annual forages both greatly lengthens the grazing season and increases and stabilizes animal performance.
- That weeds are a valuable forage and a great soil builder.
- That giving livestock periodic access to deep-rooted plants and trees improves their health.
- That the use of early season grazing can prevent lodging in small grains.
- That bloat is primarily caused by poor soil mineralization.
- That pigs can remove weeds, build soil fertility, and renovate pastures with their snouts.
- That haystacks produce the highest quality hay, which can, and should be, consumed on site.
- That pasture silage is the best way to capture and utilize high-quality surplus spring forage.
- That small cows return more profit per acre than large cows.
- And of course the ultimate truth, that healthy soils grow healthy plants, which grow healthy animals.

In today's era of omega-3 and conjugated linoleic acid research, we now know that these healthy animals also create healthy humans with their milk and meat.

It has long concerned me that alternative agriculture still largely segregates animals and crop production just as industrial agriculture does. Hopefully, this book can help show the folly of that thinking.

Animals and the plants they graze co-evolved and are symbiotic. Together they create the first building block of sustainability — healthy soil — and they do so rather effortlessly when the plants are given time to recover after each grazing.

I certainly applaud Acres U.S.A. for republishing this farming classic. I enjoyed reading it, and I'm sure you will, too.

February 2008   ALLAN NATION
PURVIS, MISSISSIPPI

Allan Nation is the editor of The Stockman Grass Farmer,
North America's leading journal of grass-based animal agriculture.

Reading Newman Turner . . .

Modern-day readers might have to adjust their vocabulary as they read this historic work, particularly those readers in North America. Following are a few thoughts on some specific terms Turner uses:

Catarrh – read as *inflammation of a mucous membrane.*

Corn – read as *grains.*

Dredge corn – read as *mixed cereals and legumes.*

Herbal ley – Today this would be called a rotational grazing cell, a paddock, or pasture. He emphasized a mix of grasses, clover and herbs. Turner made use of standard grasses such as timothy, meadow fescue, orchard grass and perennial ryegrass. Into this he added the herbs chicory, yarrow, plantain, burnet and sheep's parsley as they are deep rooted and concentrate a wide range of minerals, more so than the grasses.

Ley – read as *temporary pasture,* or a rotational cell or paddock.

Lucerne – read as *alfalfa.*

Maize – read as *corn.*

Manuring – read as *fertilizing.* What would be called *manure spreading* in North America would be described by Turner as *manuring with FYM (farmyard manure).*

Project – read as *program.*

Pulses – read as *legumes.*

About the Author

Frank Newman Turner was one of the founders of the modern environmental movement and published some of the first organic farming and gardening magazines. He founded *The Farmer,* the first organic quarterly magazine "published and edited from the farm," became a founding council member of the Soil Association, the U.K.'s leading regulator of organic standards, and served as president of an early organic horticultural organization. As a farmer, he received numerous awards in animal breeding and horticulture. A true visionary, many of his agricultural innovations are only now being rediscovered by the new wave of organic farmers and graziers.

He was born in September 1913, the eldest son of tenant farmers near Barnsley, Yorkshire, England. After graduating in agriculture and dairying at Leeds University, he became an inspector with the Potato Marketing Board. His journalistic skills soon became apparent, and he wrote regular columns for the British publications *Farmers Weekly* and *Farmer and Stockbreeder.* He met his future wife Lorna while he was on a business trip to Cornwall, and they married in 1939.

An Independent Mind

The dedication in F. Newman Turner's first book, *Fertility Farming,* is, "To my mother, who taught me to think for myself." This quality came to the fore as World War II approached, and he registered as a conscientious objector. He had become a Quaker and attended lectures by Dick Sheppard and other prominent pacifists of the time. Humanitarian principles were to guide him for the rest of his life. In 1940, he and Lorna, with their newborn son, moved to the edge of the Chilton Polden Hills in Somerset, England, where he was to manage Goosegreen, a mixed farm of about 200 acres, for conscientious objectors. Here he began experiments in organic husbandry inspired by the writings and personal encouragement of Sir Albert Howard, the author of the classics *An Agricultural Testament* and *Farming and Gardening for Health or Disease.*

When the war ended Turner bought Goosegreen and continued his experiments in creating "health from the soil up." The plow soon became redundant. He believed that fertility lay in the subsoil and was best sustained by minimal disturbance. Deep-rooting herbal leys, or planting blends for pasture, formed the basis of healthy stock — in Turner's case a herd of prize-winning pedigree Jerseys. Ailments among the cattle and draft horses — and children — were treated by fasting, enemas and dosing with herbal infusions.

F. Newman Turner launched the magazine *The Farmer* in 1946. It soon gained a devoted, if small, following in many parts of the world. He also set up the Institute of Organic Husbandry, which presented a series of weekend courses at Goosegreen. Practical instruction was given in composting, pruning, tripoding, and silage-making while Lorna served tea with home-baked scones made from stone-ground flour. A Whole Food Society was established in 1946 to put producers in touch with consumers who wanted organic produce.

Richard de la Mare of the London publishing firm Faber and Faber, who was among many visitors to Goosegreen, persuaded Turner to write the trilogy of organic farming books published in the early '50s, *Fertility Farming, Fertility Pastures,* and *Herdsmanship.* He added the booklet *Cure Your Own Cattle* to his literary output.

At about this time, Lawrence D. Hills started writing for *The Farmer.* His great mission was to establish comfrey as a major contribution to the postwar effort to feed the world. Using the Bocking strain that he had developed, he established the Great Comfrey Race in 1954. Russian Comfrey, introduced to the U.K. in the 1870s by Henry Doubleday, a Quaker smallholder, was believed to be a valuable source of protein and animal fodder. A number of farmers and horticulturalists competed for the record yields, and Lawrence D. Hills reported on their progress in the magazine *The Farmer.*

Again, F. Newman Turner led the field, growing 23 tons of comfrey per acre at Ferne Farm, Shaftesbury, Dorset, to which the family had moved in 1953. In 1958 Lawrence Hills founded the Henry Doubleday Research Association, now named Garden Organic, and invited Turner to serve as its first president.

Natural Health for Man & Beast

Many cattlemen knew of Turner's considerable experience with the natural treatment of animals . . . and he often treated their ailing cows successfully when conventional treatments had failed. Owners asked, "My cow did so well; can you suggest anything for a problem of my own?" So Turner decided to qualify as a medical herbalist and naturopath. The farming phase of his career came to an end, and the family moved to Letchworth Garden City in Hertfordshire, about an hour outside London. Although *The Farmer* closed down, Turner continued to publish its subsection, *The Gardener,* as a monthly magazine. It was probably the first exclusively organic gardening periodical. He also edited and published *Fitness and Health from Herbs,* the magazine of the U.K.'s National Institute of Medical Herbalists.

Although he was a committed pacifist, Frank Newman Turner showed no reticence in communicating his belief that both animal and human health demanded respect for and cooperation with nature. Such ideals were at loggerheads with the powerful agrochemical and pharmaceutical industries, and Turner was no stranger to controversy. In the early 1950s, at the height of the Foot and Mouth Disease epidemic, he challenged the Ministry of Agriculture to allow him to take infected animals into his herd to prove the immunity of naturally reared stock. They refused, of course, preferring to pursue the expensive slaughter policies which still continue in the Foot and Mouth and BSE crises of our day.

His innate pugnacity, the stresses inherent in his various enterprises, not least the problems of publishing on a shoestring, and what turned out to be a genetic predisposition to heart disease, proved a lethal combination. In June 1964, while visiting herbal medicine suppliers in Germany, Turner died suddenly of a coronary thrombosis. He was 50 years old. Frank Newman Turner was one of a small band of visionaries who laid the foundations for the modern environmental revolution. He always maintained that health began in the soil, and this message continues to be carried most effectively from the grassroots — the small-scale farmers and horticulturalists who uphold organic principles. The increasing awareness of mankind's duty to nature would have delighted him.

ROGER NEWMAN TURNER, B.AC., N.D., D.O.
Letchworth Garden City, England

Roger Newman Turner, the eldest of F. Newman Turner's three sons, is a practicing naturopath, osteopath and acupuncturist. He speaks and writes on complementary and alternative therapies for human health.

Contents

Part One

WHY FERTILITY FARMING?

Part Two

PRACTICAL FARM MANAGEMENT

Part Three

GOING FERTILITY
FIFTY-TWO WEEKS' FERTILITY FARMING

Part Four

THE LIVESTOCK

Part Five

ANIMAL DISEASES

THEIR PREVENTION AND TREATMENT BY NATURAL
METHODS, AND WITH THE AID OF HERBS

APPENDICES

Illustrations

PLATES

PLANS

ACKNOWLEDGEMENTS

Photographs of plates la, 2a, 5a, 8b, 12, 14a, 16, and 20 by the author: plate 15c by D. A. Guest, Edlington, Doncaster: plate 21b by Herbert, Weymouth; a by *Farmer's Weekly;* plate 16b by the *News Chronicle:* all other photographs by Douglas Allen, Bridgwater.

Preface

Fertility Farming owes its existence to the inspiration of Sir Albert Howard, whose guidance and encouragement was the starting point of much of the work which it describes. When he urged me to write a book about my work at Goosegreen, he knew that my full-time occupation as a working farmer would make its completion a matter of years; yet he went to considerable lengths to persuade me that it was a duty which must be fulfilled. I shall always regret that I was unable to complete the book before his death in 1947; but he firmly deprecated claims and reports without the basis of solid practical results, so I have used this as the measure of all my work rather than rush into print with extravagant claims and statements. *Fertility Farming* is thus essentially practical, and omits any of my work or treatments which have not yet been proved by the test of success over a number of years. This applies in particular to the section describing my treatments for the main cattle diseases; for any unproven claim in this respect would discount the rest of my farming system which I believe to be basic to the future maintenance of animal health.

Practical farming and animal husbandry have been my life work since I was born the son of a Yorkshire tenant farmer. My scientific training in the agricultural departments of two universities was an interlude from farm work which helped me the more to understand to what extent and in which way modern farming has gone wrong. From this foundation the practical development of the system of fertility farming was a natural and consequently easy process. But the recording of this work in book form would not have been possible without the cooperation and generous assistance of many friends; to the following in particular I must pay my grateful tribute. My wife and sons for their patient consideration and help in spite of frequent neglect of them during the writing of the book; Rae Thompson, for her devotion to the work of typing and retyping the manuscript at all hours of day and night, and for shouldering many other tasks to relieve me for writing; Juliette de Bairacli Levy, whose knowledge of veterinary herbs has been

xxiii

continuously at my disposal; Lawrence D. Hills, for reading the manuscript and making many detailed and valuable suggestions and for information about Russian Comfrey. I am also grateful to Malcolm Messer, the Editor of *The Farmers' Weekly,* for permission to use some material which I first wrote for his journal; to Edward Faulkner for many clues to success provided by his book *Plowman's Folly*; to Douglas Allen for most of the photographs; and to the many farmers and breeders who provided 'incurable' cattle for my work on animal diseases.

F. NEWMAN TURNER

Goosegreen Farm,
near Bridgwater, Somerset,
February 1951.

PART 1

Why Fertility Farming

CHAPTER ONE

Getting Goosegreen Back to Life

When I came to Goosegreen Farm the first calf born was dead. Disease was already master of the farm. Was I to be man enough to face such a master and turn his efforts to my own advantage? I thought I was, but disease drained the resources of the farm for nearly five years, ruining nearly two herds of cattle in the process, before I reached a position of stability in the health and production of the farm.

In February 1941, with an agricultural training at university, and the experience gained from working in agriculture all my life, I took on the management of the farm. (Subsequently I rented it, then I bought it.) My training had been orthodox, and although my ideas had been modified by contact with, and experience of, the value of natural methods of farming and livestock management, policy was controlled by the owners of the farm, so the methods of the man who had farmed the place for the twenty-five years previous to 1941 were more or less continued.

The cattle had lived and produced milk on the same pastures for generations. The hay that the mowing pastures produced could better have served the purpose of wire, for all its nutritional value. Arable crops were heavy enough, as crops grown with ample artificial manures at first are, but a variety of crop diseases were evident and showing signs of increase. The cattle were good milkers as commercial herds go, as well they should have been, for their main article of diet was purchased imported concentrated high-protein feeding stuffs, upon which the cows were forced to the limit of their capacity to produce milk and calves. The more milk the cows gave, the less natural bulky food they were allowed to eat, and what home-grown food they had was raised with artificial manures.

Governed by the instructions of the committee representing the owners, I farmed on orthodox lines. We purchased all the artificials that could be got, and by placing orders with several firms got rather more

3

than our share, much to my subsequent regret. We tried to be good farmers according to orthodox standards, and our reward was a trading loss of £2,000 for two years during the piping days of war, abortion in 75 percent of our cows, 50 percent of our total stock reactors to the tuberculin test and a large acreage of corn ruined with smut and take-all diseases, with chocolate spot making bean growing impossible.

When at the beginning of 1943 I had the opportunity to take the farm over on my own, I knew that half the cattle were barren and that I had a long history of disease to tackle. But I had faith in nature. The fact that not all the cattle had succumbed to contagious abortion and tuberculosis led me to believe that disease was not primarily caused by bacteria, but that it was the result of deficiency or excess of wrong feeding and wrong management, with bacteria only a secondary factor. Nature provides the means of combating all the disease that any living thing is likely to encounter, and I have discovered that bacteria are the main means of combating disease and not the cause of it as we had formerly believed.

So I decided to get my farm and its livestock back to nature. I would manure the fields as nature intended; I would stop exhausting the fertility of my fields and give them the recuperative benefit of variety. My cows would no longer have to act as machines, with compound cakes going in at one end and milk and calves coming out at the other. I would return them as nearly as possible to their natural lives. The more natural parts of their diet—leys, green fodder, other bulky foods and herbs—would be assured and adequate quantities insisted upon before any concentrates were fed. All the food the cows and other livestock received would be home grown, on land filled with farmyard manure, compost and green crop manure.

Artificial fertilizers, which had left my soil solid and impossible to live in, for almost any form of soil life, were dispensed with entirely. Not only because I was at last convinced of the disaster they had brought upon me, but because I could no longer afford to buy them.

There was not enough ordinary muck to go round. But with the rapid ploughing up programme that the poor grass made necessary, and the consequent increase of arable acreage, straw was accumulating. Instead of tying up the cows in the winter they were given freedom and turned loose in yards, being milked in a milking parlour. Quickly the straw stacks diminished, not in smoke as so often happens on so-called progressive farms these days, but, by way of the cattle yards, they grew into tons and tons of compost which went to produce whole-wheat to grind into flour for bread, whole oats and beans to be ground for cattle food, and fresh greenstuff for all living things on the farm—soil, cattle and men.

This kind of farming restored life to a dying farm. Everything on the farm, from the soil teeming with life and fertility, to the cows all pregnant or in full milk, and to the farmer and his family full of energy and good health, acclaim the rightness of this policy.

My neighbours have, of course, questioned the financial wisdom of such a system of farming. They said that labour for composting would be higher than the cost of buying and spreading artificial fertilizers, and yields could not possibly compare. Costs certainly did appear to increase, for it seemed that we spent more time about the muck heap, and spreading the compost, than ever we did about handling artificial manures. But when it came to be worked out, the extra cost was nothing; for the men were engaged on the muck during wet weather, and at times when there was no other productive work for them to do. Previously we must have wasted a good deal of time on worthless jobs, when now all our spare time was building up fertility at no extra cost. I shall show in this book how it is possible for the average medium-sized farm to be self-supporting in fertility, and consequently free of disease, with less capital outlay, a reduction in labour costs, and an immense saving in the cost of manures and veterinary and medicine bills.

But though there was a reduction in costs, there was a marked increase in yields. My threshing contractor tells me that my yields are not equalled in the district. Yet all my neighbours boast that they use all the artificial fertilizers they can lay hands on.

But it is not in increased yields, or in costs, that I measure the success of this organic fertility farming, though these things are important in times of economic stress. It is the health of all living things on the farm that proclaims nature's answer to our problems. From a herd riddled with abortion and tuberculosis, in which eight years ago few calves were born to full time, and those few that reached due date were dead, I can now walk around sheds full of healthy calves, and cows formerly sterile, now heavy in calf or in milk. I have advertised in the farming press for sterile cows and cows suffering from mastitis and have bought many pedigree animals, declared useless by vets, given them a naturally grown diet, and a period of fasting, herbal and dietary treatment which I have discovered to be effective in restoring natural functions, and they have subsequently borne calves and come to full and profitable production or had their udders restored to perfect health. Cows that have been sterile for two and three years have given birth to healthy calves. On the orthodox farm there is no hope for these cases, and the animals are slaughtered as 'barreners.' But nature intended the cow to continue breeding into old age, and if treated as nature intended there is every chance that her breeding capacity can be restored. I considered my pedigree Jersey cattle worth keeping and bringing back to production, and if I could buy similar animals with which others had failed, it was also doing good to myself as well as the condemned cows; and it has paid me both financially and in moral satisfaction. I have cows aged fourteen to twenty years which, after being sterile for years, have given birth to strong calves and milked well afterwards.

In the process of all this work I have experimented with the use of herbs, in the treatment of animal disease, and discovered ways in which this science can be of use to the farmer in a fix with disease. I shall say something about such treatment in a part of this book, but I should stress at the outset that the main purpose of my book is to demonstrate the simplicity and effectiveness of farming by the laws of nature; and above all to show that it can be done on the poorest of farms, by the poorest of men.

Such restoration of a dead farm is an achievement worth any man's efforts, and success within the reach of any farmer who will turn back to fertility farming, and eschew the 'get-rich-quick' methods of commercialized science, which are in fact a snare.

CHAPTER TWO

Cash Comparisons

I am not the first farmer to be unable to pay his fertilizer bill, and I shall certainly not be the last if the townsman's demand for cheap food grows. But letting hedges spread and weeds get out of hand doesn't help the bank overdraft; and merely cutting out artificials doesn't increase the yields. I had to *farm* my land and livestock out of their disaster, and I did.

For reasons which I shall explain in the next chapter, I adopted the following principles which together constitute what I have called 'Fertility Farming.' On my Somerset soil they pay both in cash and in the satisfaction of healthy crops and stock which to the true farmer is as essential a part of success as financial prosperity. There is no reason that I know why they should not give the same, or indeed better, results in different hands, on any farm in the world, with modifications to suit individual fields and conditions. I reached these conclusions after many years of experiment and five years' success on a part of the farm, all of which is now run on this system.

1. That only on land which is not adequately supplied with organic matter and is in consequence too hard and lifeless to make a seed bed, need the plough be used again. In building up to this soil condition the plough does occasionally need to be used, for instance in breaking grassland.

2. Worry about the weather can be at an end. The weather is *my* best friend, come drought, come rain, my crops will grow as nature intended—from the organic moisture-laden and nutriment-rich sponge surrounding the roots.

3. Although I have used weeds for years in the making of compost, they had been something of a pest when in competition with my crops. Now they no longer offend, for without ploughing, they can be controlled with ease and they become the providers of health and sustenance for my crops, whenever I care to use them. They are the servant of the farmer; nature's free contribution to the self-sufficiency of the farm.

7

4. Without the plough it is possible to eliminate all the other opera-tions made necessary by the plough—rolling, harrowing, cultivating, and all the clod-breaking and levelling processes needed to turn the effects of the plough back to a surface suitable for sowing.

5. The disc harrow is the key implement on the farm and as far as preparations for seeding are concerned, the only essential one. Properly used, the disc will cut all kinds of green manure or other organic manure fine enough to allow the passage of the drill. Whenever the surface trash is troublesome, until such time as a suitable drill is on the market, I can broadcast the seed and disc it in.

6. The farming community can dispense immediately with the immense financial burden of chemical manures, anti-weed and anti-pest sprays; for crops grown this natural way, with only occasional use of the plough, are adequately sustained and maintained in health and free from weeds by nature's foolproof process.

7. Drainage problems sink into obscurity. All the paraphernalia of pipes and moles and tiles and trenches, with the immense labour and machinery costs involved in providing and maintaining farm drainage systems, may be dispensed with in properly afforested areas. For, of course, we must not forget that however good our farming, deforesta-tion will bring it to naught. Except in flood and treeless areas, a soil containing adequate organic matter in the right place will attend to its own drainage problems. The man-made drain knows only how to dis-pose of water, which may later be needed to save the crop from death.

8. All organic matter should be applied to the surface, preferably as mature compost, though if it is kept on the surface where nature always puts it, applying it in an undecayed state may be permitted; in the pres-ence of ample air the process of decay will continue without robbing the growing crop and adequate nutriment will be gathered from the air. Organic matter on the surface can be used with the greatest possible speed and economy by the soil bacteria and fungi, and will itself absorb from the air, by means which I must leave the scientists to explain, not only nitrogen but also other elements essential to plant nutrition, and in the process of decay release unavailable minerals.

9. Fundamental to, and perhaps the most important essential of this system, is the fullest possible use of herbs, especially in the diet of the animals in the leys. Because of the deep-rooting abilities of practically all perennial herbs, which are the kind included in leys, they bring up and prepare without extra cost to the farmer, the essential vitamins and minerals which the foolish farmer and consumer buy at great cost in

bags and packets. These first benefit the cow when she eats the herbs and subsequently add minerals to the top soil when she deposits her dung.

10. A healthy man has all kinds of germs in his mouth and his system, yet daily explodes the old-fashioned theory of bacterial infection by his continuing health and his resistance to so-called attack from these germs. In the same way healthy crops and stock, grown by these methods, are not infected by disease, and only rarely by pests.

The Economics of Fertility Farming

The effect of applying these principles has resulted in some remarkable economies and profits which compare well with any orthodox chemically stimulated farm. It is interesting to compare some of the costs and savings.

The greatest saving is on labour and power. There is also an immense saving of tractor fuel, for instance, in the fields which have been prepared for seeding with four times disc harrowing, as against once or twice ploughing, plus three or four times discing, dragging, cultivating, rolling and all the operations that are made necessary by ploughing.

On my own farm in 1942, with half the farm under crops, I had a regular staff of eight men with seventy head of commercial cattle. Today, with a pedigree herd of eighty to ninety Jerseys and the whole farm under a four-year-ley rotation, I have a regular staff of three men, none of whom had any experience of farming before they came here.

In the matter of yields, on land which has formerly been incapable of average crops without artificial fertilizers, it may seem reasonable to expect yields to be reduced slightly in the first year without them, and again in the second year, while organic matter is being built up. But on my land the fall in yields did not take place, for the crops which required most fertility were taken on the best fields, and undersowing with a legume benefited cereal crops even in the first year. The retention of organic matter on the surface by omitting the plough was also the equivalent of a dressing of manure, even where nothing was applied.

It was this last point which really solved for me the problem of any time lag in a change over from orthodox to fertility farming methods. The avoidance of ploughing is not only an immense economy, but has the same effect on crop yields as a dressing of fertilizers. It allows organic matter to remain on or near the surface where, in the process of decay, it releases the minerals which, when the plough is used, are not available because the organic matter does not effectively release or obtain the minerals without ample air (see Chapters 3 and 4).

Some idea of my economies in cropping are shown in the following comparisons in which I take as examples ten-acre fields cropped to potatoes and then to wheat.

POTATOES OR KALE

Operations which were necessary on my farm before the changeover:

ORTHODOX FARM	£	s.	d.	2006* £	$
The fields would usually be cultivated after harvest, which would amount to about the same cost as discing	5	0	0	123	227
The field would be ploughed in the autumn at 30s. an acre	15	0	0	370	681
Then farmyard manure would be applied. I think we could reckon that labour involved in carting and spreading raw farmyard manure, as distinct from compost, would be at least £5 more, so that the cost of spreading we could put at	15	0	0	370	681
The field would be ploughed again	15	0	0	370	681
On my heavy land the amount of discing that was required to prepare a seed-bed after ploughing was at least three or four times. I found that with ploughing, all the operations of discing and preparing a seed-bed were, if anything increased, because of the tendency of the land to bake after ploughing, whereas one might have quite loose soil after discing only. If dry weather follows ploughing it is very often an even bigger job. Then, after discing, the field would need to be harrowed and, in fact, it is generally harrowed whether needed or not. There is a tendency with orthodox farmers very often to go through certain routine operations because it is the done thing. Because it has been done for generations we farmers tend to go on, year after year, doing the same thing. We must nowadays consider what operations can be done without. So that we needed, therefore, discing twice, at a cost of	10	0	0	247	460
Ridging once	10	0	0	247	460
Horse hoeing	2	0	0	49	91
The highest cost of all, with land cropped in the orthodox manner for potatoes or kale, is hand hoeing and singling—about £5 an acre	50	0	0	1,235	2,272
	£122	0	0	3,012	5,553

10

FERTILITY FARM	£	s.	d.	2006* £	$
Now I disc in the autumn at a cost of 10s. an acre	5	0	0	123	227
Compost would be applied at an approximate cost for labour of	10	0	0	247	454
And in the spring I would allow for discing approximately four times	20	0	0	494	909
I am allowing for what I would consider to be the maximum. Four times is probably more than would be needed for clean land, but four times would cover most requirements					
Then there would be sowing of seed at a cost of	2	0	0	49	91
A total for 10 acres of	£37	0	0	914	1,681

Editor's note: The author's historic financial data was converted to modern currencies and approximately adjusted for inflation, using the consumer price index. This most certainly will not correlate to modern costs and prices, but should be utilized for general directional trends only.

This brings the operation costs by fertility farming methods to £37, and under orthodox methods to £122—a difference of £85 for the ten acres or £8 to £9 an acre. This does not take account, for the orthodox farm, of spraying which costs an additional several pounds—say a modest figure of £3 an acre—making a cost of £11 an acre more than by my method. For we never find spraying necessary as we keep our own organically grown seed year after year. Our average yield of main crop potatoes is, nevertheless, anything from fifteen to twenty tons an acre.

Wheat After Any Crop Except a Ley

For wheat, the difference is not so great, but with a crop like wheat, which, unless one takes advantage of its triple purpose (grazing, grain and straw), is not a profitable crop, the smallest saving is important.

ORTHODOX FARM	£	s.	d.	2006* £	$
My methods before I adopted organic farming were to plough at least once—which for 10 acres would cost	15	0	0	370	681
It was then necessary to disc four or five times, say	20	0	0	494	909
Harrowing twice	10	0	0	247	454
Sowing	5	0	0	123	227
Harrowing again	5	0	0	123	227
Then following in spring with harrowing and rolling at a cost of £5 each	10	0	0	247	454
That is a total for 10 acres of	£65	0	0	1,605	2,953

On the fertility farm I find that it is not necessary to roll as well as harrow. If the organic content of the soil is high, the soil does not pack, so rolling is sufficient; if the organic content is low, harrowing only is sufficient. The operations are:

FERTILITY FARM	£	s.	d.	2006* £	$
Twice discing of the stubble of previous crop	10	0	0	247	454
Sowing	5	0	0	123	227
Discing	5	0	0	123	227
Harrow or roll in the spring	5	0	0	123	227
	£25	0	0	617	1,136

*Editor's note: The author's historic financial data was converted to modern currencies and approximately adjusted for inflation, using the consumer price index. This most certainly will not correlate to modern costs and prices, but should be utilized for general directional trends only.

Comparing these operations there is a difference of £40 on the ten acres.

Additionally on the orthodox farm there is the operation of spraying with selective weed killers at a cost of at least £3 an acre, which though not done every time is increasingly advocated as general practice. This would add a further £30 to the cost, an expense which I would never tolerate for it would deprive me of weeds which are needed later, in the stubble. This will bring the difference in cost to £70—or £7 an acre.

CASH COMPARISONS

The general criticism of organic methods is the cost of making compost and spreading it. But in comparison one can reckon that the cost of artificials on most farms would more than pay for a man for a whole year making compost. Certainly on my farm our expenditure on fertilisers under orthodox methods was equal to far more than the wages of *two* men. It is reasonable then to say that in avoiding an artificials bill one could quite easily devote that money to the employment of at least one full-time man doing nothing but making and spreading compost. I therefore set the cost of fertilizers to balance out the so-called extra cost of making compost, though in practice I have not found that compost making is an extra cost.

The veterinary bills, of course, are a considerable item. In my experience I have found that they can be almost completely eliminated. In the first two years of farming at Goosegreen we paid out £250 in vet's bills; in the financial years ending 31st March 1949, £20, and 31st March 1950, only £11. In the latter years practically all veterinary costs were for testing cattle for sale or for my own research purposes. On the orthodox farm routine vaccination (which we have found to be unnecessary) is a costly item, not only directly but in the breeding troubles which I believe it causes. If, for instance, we were vaccinating at Goosegreen, it would cost about £30 a year, and inevitably we should have additional consequential costs. Here, therefore, is a considerable saving for anyone practising fertility farming methods. In addition, one gets the increased return from the longer life of the cattle. We expect our cows at Goosegreen to average at least ten lactations instead of the usual three, and there is no reason why the average cow should not do the same, properly managed.

SILAGE *v.* HAY

Silage versus haymaking is an opportunity for another considerable saving in labour costs. In order to make hay one needs a large staff available at the time to take advantage of the weather, so that one needs to have men in reserve at that time of the year. With silage, I find that two men going on steadily with perhaps the assistance of a boy in between milkings, making silage regardless of weather, costs are remarkably low. Two men go out in the morning with tractor and trailer, cut enough for the day and rake it up, then the third man joins them and they go on for the rest of the day carting it in. They can go on regardless of the weather, whereas in haymaking the amount of labour is much greater. I manage to make 300 to 400 tons a year with three men, and shall

13

increase this to 500 tons next year. With the latest hydraulic lifts and green-crop loaders only two men are needed.

AVOIDANCE OF THRESHING

By harvesting oats slightly green on tripods and feeding them whole in the sheaf I have reduced threshing from fourteen days to six days a year, while at the same time increasing yields. Threshing costs £20 a day, which means a saving of £160 a year on the cost of threshing.

On my 180-acre farm the annual savings, compared with orthodox methods, quite apart from any benefits in crop yields and cattle health which may result, are approximately as follows:

	£	2006* £	$
Root and kale crops, 10 acres	120	2,963	5,452
Cereals, 80 acres, say 5 an acre	400	9,876	18,172
Threshing	160	3,950	7,269
Veterinary costs	50	1,235	1,235
Staff reductions, say	500	12,345	22,715
Annual saving on the fertility farm of 180 acres	£1,230	30,369	54,842

Editor's note: The author's historic financial data was converted to modern currencies and approximately adjusted for inflation, using the consumer price index. This most certainly will not correlate to modern costs and prices, but should be utilized for general directional trends only.

These are merely operational savings. There are in addition the saving on chemical fertilizers and feeding stuffs which would amount to at least another £1,000 to £1,200 a year on my farm if I weren't self-supporting.

In addition to initial capital economies, which are set out in the chapter 'Going Fertility,' if we assume say only £1,200 a year as the saving which can be made by eliminating unnecessary operations, it will make quite useful pin money for the missus, and you could then keep all your ordinary farm profits to share between yourself and the nation!

The following profits on the cattle account, the main branch of my farming business, and the milk production, indicates more clearly than any of my arguments the effect of these methods on the financial side of the farm in the years 1945–50.

Year Ending	March 1945	March 1946	March 1947	March 1948	March 1949	March 1950
Cattle Account	£292 (loss)	£1,182 (profit)	£381 (loss)	£2,923 (profit)	£2,436 (profit)	£2,030 (profit)
Milk Production	£1,357	£1,579	£1,843	£1,750	£2,174	£3,150

Year Ending	March 1945	March 1946	March 1947	March 1948	March 1949	March 1950
Cattle Account*	£9,032 (loss)	£35,141 (profit)	£10,700 (loss)	£76,458 (profit)	£61,993 (profit)	£50,121 (profit)
Milk Production*	£41,972	£46,944	£51,760	£45,775	£55,325	£77,774

Year Ending	March 1945	March 1946	March 1947	March 1948	March 1949	March 1950
Cattle Account*	$16,618 (loss)	$64,660 (profit)	$18,584 (loss)	$140,683 (profit)	$114,066 (profit)	$92,223 (profit)
Milk Production*	$77,229	$86,377	$95,238	$84,227	$101,798	$143,105

*Editor's note: The author's historic financial data was converted to modern currencies and approximately adjusted for inflation, using the consumer price index. This most certainly will not correlate to modern costs and prices, but should be utilized for general directional trends only.

The 1947 cattle income was reduced by a stabilization in that year with a restriction on sales and a number of purchases for breeding purposes. This resulted in a small loss on the cattle account.

The slight fall in cattle profits for 1949 and 1950 were due to the valuer's anticipation of some fall in values and a deliberate adjustment to meet this possibility. The milk production in these years gives the real picture of the herd, bearing in mind there was no feeding for high yields and that the cattle were all fed off the produce of the farm. There was *no* leakage from disease which has the most telling influence on milk output. In comparison with many high yielding herds, which use large quantities of purchased concentrates, milk output, though averaging over £110 a cow, could have been higher. But self-sufficiency in feeding stuffs and fertility would have been sacrificed. Output must be related to the cost of achieving it in feeding stuffs and veterinary bills.

What is not shown in the accounts, but what gives the only *permanent* indication of the success of these methods, is the improvement in the value of the land.

When Sir Albert Howard first stayed with us his most pertinent question after a tour of the farm was 'Do you own the farm?' 'No,' said I. 'Well, you must,' he said. 'You are putting thousands of pounds into the value of this farm by these methods, and though you can't help but make cash profits with your methods, you must also put the fertility you're building into your own pocket.' I agreed and raised the money to buy the farm.

The farm was purchased in 1941, when I started as manager, for £7,500. I gave £10,400 for it in 1946. It was valued in 1950 at £19,500. I am told that certain further improvements, since that valuation, make it now worth £25,000. This means, in any case, that since I started, its value has increased by over £17,000. Some of this is due to general increase in land values, but I am assured by those who know, that the actual value of the farm, quite apart from market changes, is at least double what it was when I took it over as a 'C' farm ten years ago. And that to me is the true farm profit, for it is the only accurate way of measuring a farmer's success.

All my facts and figures are merely those of an ordinary working farmer and are no more accurate or elaborate. As statistics they are no doubt not of the right variety, not being the products of triplicated trial plots and the like, and I am sure they are most inefficiently presented. A research station would have weighed and measured everything, sampled and analysed it to its last definable ingredient, and would probably find me several points too pessimistic. But my experiences have convinced *me* that under ordinary farm conditions most practical farmers, with no better equipment, knowledge, or ability than their neighbours, would with fertility farming, produce even better results, and with modifications to suit individual farms they would produce them anywhere in the world.

CHAPTER THREE

Basis of Fertility Farming

I cannot expect any farmer to believe that my results are other than the result of luck, good land, and perhaps the special Providence that looks after fools, much less try them on his own farm, without giving the scientific principles on which they are based. Justifications for the greatly increasing numbers of organic farmers, those who in this country and all over the world are now eliminating the plough (see *Plowman's Folly* by Edward Faulkner), and the many farmers and authorities who have abandoned artificial fertilizers as a snare and a danger to health, in favour of entirely organic methods, will be found in the next chapter.

Here I am concerned only with the strictly orthodox explanations, established by research stations, mainly Rothamsted; it makes no difference to my results which are the right reasons. It is even possible that both are entirely wrong, but far more likely that each is correct in some places and not in others.

In theory, by not using artificial fertilizers, and not importing feeding stuffs to my farm, I am exhausting its fertility. Even if I return the straw to the land, a crop of wheat of 2 ton 2 cwt. to the acre takes of 50 lb. nitrogen (roughly as much as $4^1/_2$ cwt. of sulphate of ammonia contains), $28^3/_4$ lb. potash, 21 lb. of phosphoric acid (phosphorus) and 9.2 lb. of calcium.[1] Grass makes even heavier demands: a $1^1/_2$-ton crop of hay removes 49 lb. of nitrogen, 32.1 lb. of lime and 12.3 lb. of phosphoric acid.

All these elements, in natural form, available to plant life, are going off my farm with everything I sell. Every gallon of milk and every animal I market removes calcium and phosphorus, yet despite the additional losses from 'plant foods' washing out in drainage water, I still have more than I started with.

---

[1] *Manures & Fertilizers,* Sir Daniel Hall, p. 22 (John Murray).

WHY FERTILITY FARMING?

The explanation is known to every agricultural student; the amount of the heaviest dressing of any artificial fertilizer we can apply to balance the income and expenditure of the land is tiny compared to the vast reserves which lie in the top nine inches of all but the most infertile soil, and in the air above the soil, provided the soil bacteria are adequate to gather it to the soil. The famed Broadbalk field at Rothamsted, after bearing wheat for 100 years, with no manure of any kind and an average crop of $12\frac{1}{2}$ bushels an acre, still contains in its top soil 2,500 lb. nitrogen, 2,750 lb. phosphoric acid and 6,750 lb. potash. The next nine inches probably has nearly as much, and a deep-rooting herb or a tree root going down as far as six feet or more can tap untold reserves.

There is no possible doubt, that what matters in the growing of crops for ourselves and our stock, is the amount of the essential elements which are available for use, including the trace elements which have the importance of vitamins, and the plant hormones about which we are now beginning to know more and which are present only in the living humus of the soil. Not only does this prove that it is possible to farm as I farm on the fertility of my soil, and the provisions of the air above my soil made available by the surface organic matter, it proves that even the poorest soils can be farmed in this way if the system of cultivation is designed to build up the amount of available plant foods near the surface, and keep the land in that same condition which allows nature to grow healthy oak trees for hundreds of years in the same place without importation of fertilizers. The only manures that come on to my farm are sewage sludge and sawdust, and though there may only be $1\frac{1}{4}$ lb. of phosphoric acid in 1 cwt. of sewage sludge, the organic matter must supply more and obtain more from its surroundings, and by returning to my land what should rightly go back to it, I am saving my sons, and the men who will farm my lands 500 years in the future, from the disaster of soil exhaustion.

I am therefore clearly justified, in theory, by high authority. But I don't believe a word of it. I was *justified* before I started my 'unorthodox' methods, yet my land suffered. The reserves in the soil are the amounts which will dissolve in hydrochloric or sulphuric acid, but crops don't use either of these acids. In theory it would be equally possible to get all the essential elements to support the human body into several pills a day, with results as serious to health as the ease with which the chemical substitute for the real thing is produced.

I can disc in weeds and green manure crops, and use sawdust, without a fall in yield from lack of nitrogen, as the cellulose and carbohydrate decomposing bacteria increase and take it out of the soil and the air to make up their bodies, because I have in my topsoil unlimited natural nitrogen in the forms which plants can use.

This, apart from legume nitrogen bacteria, is fixed by azotobacter croccoceum and other free nitrogen fixers, the bacteria to which almost all the combined nitrogen in the world is owed—sulphate of ammonia was originally fixed by coal-measurage bacteria. Firstly we gain this in the compost heap. Up to 40 percent of the nitrogen in normal farmyard manure is lost in making and storage; yet the compost heap gains up to 26 percent from the air through the activity of azotobacter and its allies which cannot work in the anaerobic conditions of the orthodox dung heap. The compost heap, then, not only adds the additional plant foods gathered by weeds as well as straw; the power of the sun, stored in the carbohydrates in the heap, sets the azotobacter-fixing nitrogen, till there is more in the finished article than there was in the original dung. (See *The Waste Products of Agriculture* by Sir Albert Howard and K. Wad.)

Further, when compost is spread on the surface of the soil, and not ploughed in, it has the ability of increasing not only the nitrogen content of the soil, but also the phosphorus and calcium and potash. My knowledge of science is insufficient to explain why. As far as I know they do not exist in the air, though that would seem to be the only source from which the organic matter can absorb them. Maybe dust particles in the air carry phosphorus, potash and calcium, or maybe some scientist will discover that even the air in conjunction with organic matter is able to create them. The fact is that they appear in abundance where surface organic matter is adequate and they benefit the crop in a way which is not evident when organic matter is ploughed down or when these elements are applied in artificial form.

Compost is today, in terms of labour, relatively costly, though not more so than the practice of yarding bullocks for dung. But compost is of far greater value than dung as applied from a normal heap, and my methods greatly increase its effectiveness without increasing labour costs.

The surface of the soil is the natural place for humus; all decayed vegetation starts there, and with ample air and the high pH, it makes a bacterial hotbed; decay is almost all aerobic. The azotobacters supply unlimited nitrogen, and the compost is thus almost as quickly available as an artificial fertilizer, but it is instead a perfect diet. Further, any kind of organic matter applied direct to previously composted land, so rich in bacteria and nitrogen, is attacked as readily as in a compost heap, making what is known as sheet composting almost as effective, though not quite so quick, as the application of mature compost.

The darkening of my soil by humus also helps. The sun warms it up quicker, and azotobacter work best between 50° F. and 60° F. Underground it takes longer to warm up, and there is less oxygen. The lime still in the compost keeps the pH about neutral, which the azotobacter need. There are a host of bacteria in any fertile soil, of equal or greater importance than the fungi; a Rothamsted direct count[1] showed 3,733,000,000 per gram of soil from a farmyard manure plot, 1,766,000,000 per gram on complete artificials, 1,000,000,000 per gram no manure.

Rothamsted showed, therefore, that by using artificials nearly 2,000,000,000 unpaid helpers are discarded from every gram of soil (about a saltspoon full), and instead the fertilizer maker and the chemist are paid to do their job far less efficiently; for as with all bad workmen, it costs even more to repair their mistakes.

The plant foods from this humus layer are available at root level, and the quick growth of weeds between crops acts as a storehouse for the excess, particularly in late summer. Nature will not tolerate bare ground, because it wastes this store. The bacteria have a peak of late summer activity, and if the ground is clear it will wash away. If weeds are used, as I describe in a later chapter, they catch this surplus nitrogen for the subsequent crop.

Nitrogen is important firstly because, unless there is enough in the land, no other elements can be taken up. Artificial nitrogen fertilizers are the most lethal destroyers of soil organisms and fungi—sulphate of ammonia even being sold as a worm killer—and because they are plentiful, they are pushed by commercial undertakings and, sad to say, even by the Ministry of Agriculture; but in artificial form they are pure disease creators. At Goosegreen we have got nature's nitrogen supply taped; that is one of our great key advantages.

Bare land, under arable cultivation by ploughing from virgin prairie (Saskatchewan), lost 1,400 lb. more nitrogen than was recovered in the crop in twenty-two years. In the same period, at Rothamsted, land allowed to run completely wild gained 2,200 lb., 91.7 lb. a year (see *Soil Conditions and Plant Growth*). Fertility farming adds far more, but does not allow any waste.

Goosegreen is a worms' paradise, and moles also help with the drainage without causing any damage. On a farm under full cropping rotation molehills don't cause any trouble. They merely aerate the soil and improve its friability.

It may be argued that when, in the Middle Ages, we farmed with wooden ploughs which did not invert the soil, on the open-field system, grazing our weedy fallow strips and using no artificials, but returning all animal and human excrement to the soil, our crop yields were rather less than half those of the present day.

But there are very important differences, apart from improved breeds of stock and crops. Then, grain crops were weeded by hand and the weeds carried off; hoeing was practised, the disc harrow not invented, and the true compost heap, with its balance of biological activity, still not known. The modern compost heap is as important as any agricultural discovery of recent years. Though there is evidence of disease in both crops and stock in early manuscripts, it is likely that, as these have increased so greatly within living memory, on the whole, agriculture was healthier even though more people on the land produced far less. Even in the reign of Queen Anne, we exported wheat to America, to such parts as were colonized.

CHAPTER FOUR

Farming Without Plough or Chemicals

Nature does not plough; she employs the earthworm and soil bacteria, together with deeply penetrating roots, to do her work.

Nature does not supply water-soluble minerals to the soil; she ensures an automatic and ample application of organic matter which, in the process of decay, produces organic acids to act upon soil minerals and so make them capable of absorption by plant roots. Because we have failed to follow the example of nature we find that the soil in our care has apparently become incapable of providing sufficient good food to sustain our population in health. Why has the soil that was provided for our sustenance now become what the chemists call 'deficient'—unequal to the task for which it was intended? Or has it?

In modern farming, both crop production and livestock feeding, we have been concerned with the provision of prepared nutrients imported to the farm, instead of making full use of the complete provisions of nature. The result is that we have burdened farming with the colossal cost of chemical fertilizers, sprays, insecticides, vaccines and medicines, while nature quietly continues to beat us, in the matter of both abundant production and healthy crops and animals, at no cost.

The earth is the permanent possessor of all things contained therein and which grow therefrom; they are loaned to the human and animal kingdom for bodily sustenance for the duration of life, but nature decreed that they shall, after use, be returned to the earth. No plant, animal or human being can claim the right of destruction, or of permanent possession, of any of the ingredients of its food or physical body. They must be returned to fhe earth to sustain new life and to ensure the continuation of the universe when life, for us, is ended. We are but the tenants of life, having on loan the physical from the earth and the spiritual from God. What happens to our spiritual being and its inspiration remains to be discovered after we lay down the physical life. But our duties regarding the physical body and its means of natural sustenance are clear to all. It must be returned, together with all organic matter derived from the earth, back to the earth.

Problems of so-called soil deficiencies—certainly as far as the main elements are concerned—have only arisen with the increasing failure to acknowledge and act upon this law. Without adequate decaying organic matter to release, in the process of its decay, the otherwise non-available phosphates, potash and nitrogen, man has thought it necessary to transport these elements from sources of concentrated supply and, by treatment with chemicals, render them water soluble. In powder form these water-soluble elements are then applied, to upset the natural balance of the soil, to impregnate the water particles of the soil with concentrations far in excess of the optimum natural supply. Upon these the plant draws, instead of utilizing the more slowly available organic elements of the humus.

Phosphate deficiency is one of the outstanding fallacies of science (in soil as distinct from certain types of solid rock). There is no such thing; or at least none that science can measure. All that the soil analyst can measure is *availability*. When the soil analyst tells us a field is suffering from phosphate deficiency he merely means that insufficient phosphate is *available*; in other words, that the soil does not contain enough organic matter to produce the necessary mineral-releasing acids in the soil. A soil only becomes 'deficient' when there is insufficient decaying organic matter upon it to release the mineral nutrients already present in an unavailable form, and gather them from the air and falling rain.

The solution, therefore, to all apparent deficiencies, is adequate organic matter in the right place.

Experience has shown me that the right place for organic matter is on or very near the surface of the soil. That seems to be one of the reasons for the success of eliminating the plough. Whether we have applied it or not, the soil surface is usually covered with organic matter: straw-stubble, weeds, leaves and numerous minute decaying bodies and the microscopic excreta of millions of living creatures. If we plough we put this down, not only beyond the reach of most domestic plant roots, where incidentally weed seeds will be preserved, to germinate next time we plough and bring them to the surface, but at a depth which will catch moisture from above and below and withhold it from the crop which grows in the top soil.

WHY FERTILITY FARMING?

Nature accumulates organic matter on the surface, year by year, and what she needs below the surface she transports by means of earthworms and other soil organisms.

That great gardener, F. C. King, following Sir Albert Howard's imitation of nature's way of manuring by compost, perceived also that nature does not dig, and, in consequence, does not need to spray to keep her crops free from disease and parasite. He proceeded to sow his seeds in undug soil, which was abundantly supplied with organic matter. 'It is not the richness of the soil that confers immunity on plants, but rather the unity which prevails within the soil, whenever this remains undisturbed,' he said. He believes that digging damages fungi in the soil. It is reasonable to assume that the disturbance of soil severs the threads of mycelium, which convey nutriment from the humus of the soil to the rootlets of the plant—the process known as mycorrhizal association which Dr. M. C. Rayner and Sir Albert Howard have shown to be a vital necessity to the health of certainly over 80 percent and probably all of our domestic crops. My farming experience has shown me that there is an intricate and carefully balanced inter-relation of activity in the soil, which should never be disturbed, provided we can supply organic material necessary to the maintenance of this activity. I believe that if one part of the process is interrupted or prevented there is no substitute but only partial emergency measures. The process remains incomplete and the crop suffers accordingly.

Now that I have seen the remarkable crops resulting from land that has been unploughed for six years, in different fields, I can support every word of criticism which the American, Edward Faulkner, had for the plough in his book *Plowman's Folly*. When I first tried to farm without the plough I was not overwhelmed with success. I could not get a tilth fine enough to satisfy my orthodox conception of a good seed-bed. The rubbish on the surface worried me too much and I succumbed to the temptation to plough it in. I felt also that ploughing was essential in order to bring some moisture to the parched surface. The surface soil always dried out so quickly that it was often necessary to bring up the moisture from below during a dry time, before it was possible to produce a seed bed moist enough to take seed and enable it to grow away quickly from the weeds.

I was afraid that my crops would be smothered by weeds if I did not plough them under out of sight for another year; little realizing that at the same time I was bringing up last year's seeds, well preserved and in an ideal condition for immediate germination and quick growth.

24

FARMING WITHOUT PLOUGH OR CHEMICALS

So I continued to plough, until it occurred to me that when my land contained sufficient organic matter some of my earlier failures would be explained. For without adequate organic matter the soil was not in a natural condition to operate the simple process of nature. By starving the soil of organic matter and above all by transferring what organic matter there was from the surface to a site six to eight inches below the surface, I was placing beyond the reach of the crop all its nutriment and its means of conserving the moisture for root growth. I suddenly realized why weeds always grow rapidly and vigorously during the most disastrous drought, while the domestic crop shrivels and dies. Many weeds are deeper rooting than our cultivated crops, so that where land is ploughed they have continuous call on the decaying organic matter which is lying out of reach of the cultivated crop but at the optimum level for the sustenance of the weeds. The weeds, therefore, have ample moisture at their root level to keep them in continuous growth regardless of external extremes of weather and, of course, they can laugh heartily at the wretched wheat or cabbage struggling miserably in the dried-out top soil, with only the artificial additions to stimulate growth plus whatever moisture may, from time to time, fall from the sky.

I saw then why uncultivated crops rarely suffer from drought; why the forests, hedgerows and roadside weeds flourish, regardless of weather conditions, while our crops in cultivated fields grow in stops and starts, according to the weather, and in many cases don't grow at all unless we provide artificial stimulants. It becomes clear too how *we* may grow vigorous healthy crops by imitating nature and leaving the soil, as far as possible, undisturbed except on the very surface; allowing the plant to feed at the breast of nature instead of periodically severing the child from the breast and violently forcing upon it our bottle of poisonous chemicals.

So I determined, now that my soil contained more organic matter, to try again and, from a number of fields, I rested the plough. Somewhat diffidently and with apprehension—for I was still afraid of the weeds and the possible failure of the sown seeds to germinate in the rough and dry seed-bed—I wrote, in the 1948 spring number of *The Farmer*, about crops sown without ploughing in the previous year:

'Each field was given a good churning up with the cultivator and afterwards cut up as well as could be with the disc harrow. The risk was that not all the weed seeds were germinated by the time the crop was sown as there was still no rain. The crops were sown in a dry lumpy seed-bed, yet, in spite of this, excepting one piece of wheat, they all look well, though the unploughed fields are showing more than their fair quota of weeds. In the case of the oats and vetches, which are to be cut for silage in May, this does not matter for the weed will provide bulky green food, giving a variety of valuable herbs to the silage, and they will be cut before there is any chance of the seeds falling.'

'But the resulting crops astounded me and here is their history.

'The third week of September I sowed Pilot seed wheat in a field which had grown moderate crops of wheat the two previous years. This is bad farming practice of course, but I was curious to see what a third crop of wheat would do. The field had not been ploughed for thirteen months. The seed was sown in a rough knobbly seed-bed in a covering of dead and dying weeds churned up with a mixture of wheat straw stubble by the disc harrow. The tilth was rough enough to block the drill at times, but we scrambled our way through it and I prayed that rain would come to give the wheat a good start. For three weeks there was no rain and the weeds flourished. Throughout the winter it looked as though the crop would have to be resown in the spring. But when spring came the weeds were diminishing and the wheat shot forward. Before the wheat was in ear it was evident that the weeds had disappeared and the wheat was clearly one of the heaviest crops I had grown on the farm, for I had never seen such a strong and vigorous growth, without manuring of any kind, and after two previous straw crops.

'Nature had attended to the manuring by the natural death of the weeds; for the weed seeds remaining ungerminated on the surface had obviously come to maturity during the late autumn and had died off during the winter, and the acids of decay had released available minerals to provide nutriment for the flourishing wheat roots. The long dry spring and the drought of early summer left the wheat unaffected. Vigorous growth continued in consequence of the moisture and organic nutriment held at the root level of the plant by the natural sponge of decaying organic matter,'

The wheat yielded $39\frac{1}{2}$ cwt. an acre compared with 27 cwt. an acre for the first crop and 20 cwt. an acre for the second crop.

'Equally successful was a crop of oats and vetches, also sown on land that had not been ploughed for two years previously. So rapid was the growth of this crop that though we started harvesting it for silage at the optimum stage of growth, about two feet high, before we could finish the field it was over six feet high in parts and provided a tremendous tonnage of green food per acre.

FARMING WITHOUT PLOUGH OR CHEMICALS

'Encouraged by the success of the wheat and silage crop, I sowed eight acres of kale. Though one might expect a root crop to produce less spectacular results without what I have formerly assumed was the 'aid' of the plough, the results were even more encouraging than my previous ventures. The most remarkable thing was the almost complete absence of weeds in a field that was, at the outset of surface tillage methods, extremely dirty following three corn crops. The field was well disced before seeding and thistles were hoed by hand. A dressing of sewage sludge was worked in and the field received no further cultivation, not even horse hoeing or hand hoeing, other than two days work for three men cutting out a few persistent thistles.

Visitors found it difficult to believe that we had not horse or tractor hoed up and down the rows continuously throughout the growing stages of the crop. For they had seen no crop sown on ploughed land, even with continuous cleaning, that had achieved such freedom from weeds.

A COMPARISON OF PLOUGHED AND UNPLOUGHED LAND

A remarkable example of the harmfulness of the plough was accidentally provided when I ploughed an old pasture. The whole field was ploughed with the exception of one corner which had been scattered with straw and upon which grazing cattle had deposited some dung two years previously. The looseness of the top soil and the debris on the surface made the plough ineffective in this corner and the soil was merely pushed aside, to be broken down later by the disc harrow. After being worked the whole field was sown to turnips during early July. Over most of the field, in spite of continuous wet weather, the young turnips were, for ten days since they showed two leaves above ground, at a standstill, indicating that something below the surface was retarding growth. But the corner that was not ploughed and which had a supply of organic matter worked into the surface never ceased to grow, and the plants were at least three times as big as those in the rest of the field. Furthermore, unlike the unploughed kale field, the weeds in the ploughed turnip field got out of control. All the weed seeds of a generation past, since the field was last ploughed, germinated promptly on arrival at the surface of the soil and proceeded to thrust their roots down to the decaying turf, which lay below the reach of the turnips.

This solved for me a problem upon which I had previously not had the courage to risk a trial; I formerly believed that though one might dispense with the plough on stubble and following potatoes or

27

roots, it would nevertheless be necessary to plough up old pastures and temporary leys on first breaking them up. Now, once more, nature thrust this demonstration under my nose and urged me to go the whole hog. Nature permits no half measures and she clearly indicated that, if I am to farm properly, I must imitate her ways as completely as possible so far as is within my ability to perceive them. This means that no land *need* be ploughed if there is sufficient organic matter available to enable the natural cultivation of earthworms and other organisms to prepare and make friable the soil and ease the preparation of a seed-bed with disc harrows only.

PREREQUISITES OF SUCCESS

There are, however, a number of provisions upon which I would insist before entirely dispensing with the plough:

1. The plough pan—if it exists—should be broken by means of a deep subsoiler, which shatters the pan without bringing the subsoil to the surface.

2. The soil should be made crumbly and friable by the addition of organic matter before real success can be achieved. Compost is the most effective means of utilizing to the full any available organic matter and converting it to a condition which makes it perfect as a soil food and easy to spread. This need not involve any extra labour or special equipment. See Chapter 10 on compost making.

3. Every opportunity must be taken to maintain this surface organic matter by the growing of green crops for discing in between crops, and the use of deep-rooting herbal leys.

PART 2

Practical Farm Management

Having examined in some detail my system
of organic surface tillage which eliminates
the use of the plough, and which is basic
to the whole of my farming practice, I can
devote the rest of this book to practical
details of the application of the system to
my own particular farm

CHAPTER FIVE

Soil Management and Cropping Rotation

The basis of the effectiveness of nature's husbandry is a fertile soil—and the measure of a fertile soil is its content of organic matter, or ultimately its humus. Nature bases all her forms of life on humus and attempts nothing without it. Indeed, until she has created it, nature's process of plant and animal life cannot go on. Though often in later stages of the cycle of life nature is known to substitute, she has no substitute for humus—a point which is paramount to our conception of successful fertility farming.

Upon a basis of humus, nature builds a complete structure of healthy life—without need of disease control of any kind. Nature does not treat disease because she *is* the example of perfect health—disease is the outcome of the unbalancing or perversion of nature—and serves as a warning that something is wrong. Disease is the result of a removal from natural context or the withholding or perversion of natural nutriment.

The avoidance of disease is therefore the simple practice of natural law.

Upon a basis of humus, nature sows her seed—or rather the wind and the birds do it for her. There is no ploughing—no cultivation, no preparation of a seed-bed. The perfect seed-bed is the covering of organic material which has been gently laid upon the earth.

Nature does not even disturb the soil to cover her seed, but drops loosely over the seed more potential humus, in the form of leaves and twigs. Thus speedy germination is assured. Growth commences and is nurtured by various wonderful processes all automatic and adequate to the needs of the plant—not one of them is in any way capable of satisfactory substitution by man—though the scientist believes he has improved on nature's ways and that nature is no longer capable of growing abundant crops without his assistance.

But on the organic farm, substitution is never necessary. Except on the thinnest hill land, which probably should not be farmed, in any case, without long recuperative treatment, all the necessary mineral nutriment, which the soil analyst considers most important, is present, though not available until released. This is done in the process of decay of surface organic matter which in the presence of free oxygen releases carbonic acid, which in turn dissolves the minerals in the soil to make them assimilable by the plant.

The difference between this natural process of plant nutriment and the chemical methods of man, is that man provides his artificial nutriment in water-soluble form and the plant has no alternative but to absorb it if it is to take up any moisture at all—because all the water particles, known as the soil solution, in the soil hold the chemical in solution. The plant is stimulated and builds up what Sir Albert Howard called 'a bastard structure' derived from inorganic nitrogen instead of from the organic protein of the humus.

The artificial provision of soluble nutrient short circuits the mycorrhizal association previously mentioned. This is the process whereby fungal threads—known as mycelium—develop in the humus and invade the roots of the plant. This mycelium is rich in organic protein which is digested by the enzymes of the root cells. The sap then carries this nutriment to the green leaf and enables it to develop.

It is this process which is vital to the health of the plant, for it is known that it takes place only in the presence of humus and that plants deprived of it either by 'short-circuit' feeding, or by lack of humus, succumb to pests and disease.

The complete explanation of the ability of naturally fed plants to resist disease is not clear as yet. But I believe it is dependent on a supply of plant hormones from the humus to the plant and eventually to the animal and man. We know the importance of vitamins to the health of all living things. It seems certain that hormones are even more important—and there, nature is so complex that it is not possible to provide them in the right form synthetically. Attention to the organic content of the soil is therefore the only certain means of ensuring adequately the hormones that are an essential link in every phase of life. They are the life force of nature and are present only in the fresh living nutriment of plant, animal and man. They are not present in a life-maintaining and health-giving form in inorganic elements, or in material that has been mortified by excessive heat. Hence the need for fresh raw food of organic origin for all living things.

The most important aspect of surface tillage is the maintenance of surface organic matter. This is important to any type of good farming and indispensable for healthy crops; but it is an essential part of farming without the plough. For soil lacking in humus is difficult to work with *any* tool, even with the plough. It is the diminishing sponginess of soil that has contributed more than anything else to the need for more cumbersome machines and more vigorous cultivation in modern farming.

We set as our ideal of good soil the leaf mould of the forest floor. The nearer this ideal is approached on a field scale the less cultivation is needed. For such leaf mould is so porous that it does not need even stirring to incorporate air; it is already itself composed largely of air. Taken in the hand, it feels light and spongy. Seed need only be dropped in soil of this kind to find coverage, warmth and moisture, the ideal conditions for healthy vigorous growth. It is free from weed seeds because a material so full of air and nutriment, so full of moisture and dissolved mineral salts, quickly germinates any seed that may be present, bringing it to a stage when it may be destroyed if not required. Airless soil lacking in humus, on the other hand, tends to preserve weed seeds until such time as the surrounding conditions are ideal for germination and growth.

Not only is ample organic matter imperative, but it must remain on or near the surface. It is useless to apply heavy dressings of organic manure and then to plough it down out of reach of aerobic bacteria, earthworms, and other organisms of decay. At a depth greater than five or six inches at the most, depending on the type of soil, the process of decay ceases and putrefaction (i.e. decay by fungi and bacteria working without oxygen, which break it down to gases of low food value) takes place. Lower still the material tends to be preserved for long periods and only broken down as it may be allowed some contact with air as a result of subsoiling or other disturbance of the lower soil. The ideal to follow, then, in preparing a soil for sowing by the methods here described, is that which nature employs; but because of the long years of exploitation to which all our cultivated soils have been subjected, modification, to the extent of assisting mechanically the incorporation of the organic matter with the topsoil, is necessary.

The imitative processes may be summarized as follows:

Except initially when it will be necessary to break the old plough pan and admit the air to the subsoil by means of a sub-soiler, we may cease to touch the soil below a depth of three inches, except inasmuch as the deepening humus of the soil admits the disc harrow in the process of surface working. But on most farms the shattering of the subsoil *is* a necessary first step towards getting the soil right for organic surface tillage.

This work is done with a tool called a subsoiler, which is available on wheels to be trailed or as a hydraulic fitment for tractors equipped with a hydraulic power system. The active part of the tool is merely an arm which penetrates the soil to a depth of fifteen to twenty-four inches, shattering the subsoil without bringing it to the surface. This is done, generally up and down the slope where one exists, at intervals of four feet apart, or less if tractor wheels allow it without compressing the sub-soiled part.

Once each field has been subsoiled it should not be necessary to repeat the operation or to touch the subsoil in any way, at least for the duration of a rotation. If it is convenient to subsoil the land once in each rotation, that is every seven or eight years, it will be beneficial, but once deep-rooting herbal leys have been all round the farm, and are continued in the rotation, even sub-soiling should not be necessary. There is no better means of aerating the subsoil than by the roots of herbs like chicory, burnet, lucerne, and dandelion, all of which penetrate to a depth of three or four feet and more in as many years.

It is as a result of experimenting with surface tillage since 1944 that I have come to the conclusion that we can make the most economical use of available resources by maintaining an adequate supply of organic matter as a surface skin to the soil, relying on the natural action that this engenders to perform all the cultivation of aeration deeper than two to three inches.

The mere omission of the plough is in itself a contribution to the effective organic content of the soil. The solution to all mineral 'deficiencies' is adequate organic matter at the soil surface. It is on this assumption that I have restored all my 'deficiencies' without an ounce of chemical manures. Instead I have maintained the organic content of the topsoil by means of frequent green manuring or sheet composting, and by utilizing all the wastes of the farm—straw, hedge trimmings, yard scrapings, sawdust, old sacks, and a small proportion of farmyard manure—to make compost.

Green manure is provided by undersowing cereal crops with trefoil or broad red clover and Italian ryegrass, and by sowing mustard on the bare land in between crops, discing them into the surface, rather than ploughing them under where they would be useless (this is called 'sheet' composting, a term originated many years ago by Sir Albert Howard in India); for, six inches below the surface not only are green

1a. Compost is spread on stubble and disced into surface soil. Into this mulch seed is drilled or broadcast.

1b. Ley management. Topping off the ley after grazing and spreading dung droppings.

2a. The Abundance of Fertility Farming. An 84-bushels-an-acre crop of Pilot wheat grown by 'Fertility farming' methods at Goosegreen Farm.

2b. The Desolation of 'Scientific Farming.' American News Agency photograph depicting 'near record winter wheat crop averaging 18.4 bushels an acre.' (Quoting U.S. Department of Agriculture news release.)

crops or organic manures of no value to the shallow-rooting crop, but they act as an obstacle to the capillary flow of moisture to the crop. The crop is sown in the churned-up green manure on the surface, either by means of a disc drill or by broadcasting and afterwards discing if the amount of organic matter makes drilling difficult.

WEEDS

We are now realizing that we have been mistaken to regard weeds as enemies of the farm crop. Most weeds are deep rooting plants which penetrate the subsoil and bring to the surface valuable elements (not available to the shallower-rooting domestic crop) which have been plundered from the topsoil by years of exploitive methods. I have seen my Jersey cattle going around patches of nettles or docks, eating off the flowering tops and relishing something that they have been unable to obtain from the simple shallow-rooting ley mixture.

But it is difficult to make use of weeds *in* our crops and yet keep them in control. So the thing we must do is to get back into our dairy pastures as many herbs as possible, to assist the health of the cattle grazing the leys and to benefit the topsoil in a way which any amount of chemical dressing can never do. All my leys contain a high proportion of these weeds deliberately sown—burnet, chicory, plantain, wild vetch, sheep's parsley, dandelion, sweet clover, chickweed—and when the leys have been down four years and developed roots to a depth of several feet they are then most relished by cattle. The cattle did anything to get from the younger shallower-rooting leys, when I still had some, to those herbal leys that had penetrated the valuable untapped resources of the deeper subsoil.

Deep ploughing can never achieve the same effect, for the elements remain locked up until worked on by organic acids from the humus and the rootlets. Bloat has become a thing of the past since such leys were used, whereas before I lost cattle every year when I practised the method of sowing leys with three or four ingredients only. This is due partly to the more fibrous nature of the herbal ley, the more substantial growth of grasses and clovers grown in soil of high humus content, as compared with the quick-growing chemically stimulated product, and partly to the reserves of elements essential to digestion made available by the deep taproots of the herbs in the ley.

Trees

We farmers have almost forgotten about trees and our only thoughts about them nowadays are to decide how best we can cut them down, to make way for larger and more powerful machines. But the slow disappearance of trees from our farmlands has resulted in serious flood and drought problems, and in declining fertility. Trees take up moisture and hold it as required, and it is now common knowledge that the serious drought areas are those with few trees. Further, the roots of trees penetrate to a great depth, bringing up minerals and trace elements to the leaves which are subsequently deposited to contribute organic matter as well to the surrounding fields. Leaf fall may seem to be a small contribution to fertility, but it is an extremely valuable one which cannot be satisfactorily substituted artificially.

Optimum fertility is therefore as dependent on a proper proportion of the farm being devoted to trees as on the application of manures. At least one-twentieth of the farm acreage should be occupied by trees, most of which will, of course, be in hedges. If the farm carries a smaller acreage than this, immediate attention should be given to planting varieties which will have a cash value to the farm.

I am not as knowledgeable about trees as I would like to be—or as I think a good farmer ought to be. When I had my agricultural training, trees were entirely ignored as a farm crop, but they can be made a valuable cash crop apart from their fertility value, and should have serious attention as such in the future. But I have got hold of information which will enable farmers to make a useful start with trees as a crop. The society known as The Men of the Trees, founded by Richard St. Barbe Baker at The Gate, Abbotsbury, Dorset, will give any more detailed information about technical matters and sources of supply of trees.

Planting Distances. An average distance of five feet apart each way will suit nearly every timber tree. For shelter belts, make the rows six feet apart, with trees four feet apart in the rows, and the outer windward row eight feet or more apart. These distances work out at nearly 2,000 trees per acre, which allows for filling blanks.

Cultivation. Grass is a greedy enemy of young trees. The ground should be cleaned, and a crop of red clover, sown before planting, will keep the ground cool and free of weeds without smothering the young trees. Otherwise the ground between trees should be hoed the first two years.

Planting. Any soft weather between autumn and spring is suitable. The ground can be marked out with a planting marker, and trees rapidly planted at intersections. It is essential to keep tree bundles damp in bags or baskets, only exposing a few roots at a time. Avoid windy and frosty days.

Size of Trees. From eighteen inches to two feet is the best size on good soil. Scots firs are very tough, and may be smaller. Also try acorns sown in rows like peas.

Shelter Belts. For an orchard, or limited small area, a single line of trees may be used. One of the best is Lawson Cyprus or Nutka cypress. At eight feet apart they join to make a solid wall, not too high and not too thick. The usual shelter belt should be of five or six rows. The windward row should be of spruce on damp soil, of Austrian fir on dry soil, at ten feet apart to make solid trees. Between the spruce plant alternate trees of birch or poplar to nurse them. The inner rows can be of timber trees for your particular soil, chosen by an expert.

The fast growing hybrid poplars will hide a two-story row of houses in seven years. Cricket bat willows rightly treated can be ready for bats in as little as twelve years. Birch and ash can make useful farm timbers in ten years, and even oak can be useful in fifteen years if very closely planted, as it should be.

In five or six years Sitka spruce, hybrid or Japanese larch make massive young belts which will shelter stock, crops, and working yards. Your farm can be changed from bleak bareness to pleasantly dressed landscape in a dozen years, under average conditions, in less under rich conditions.

Varieties to Plant and Their Uses

Variety	Soil and Situation	Uses
Alder	Waterside tree.	Timber for underwater work, edging streams and ponds against wear; also charcoal, clogs, etc.
Ash	For waterholding limy soils.	Will always sell. Plant plenty, Coachbuilding, handles, hurdles, oars, etc.
Beech	Well drained lime soils.	Chairs, furniture, stairs, broom-heads, sleepers.
Birch	Any soil. Despised but useful. Nurse against frost for beech, spruce.	Plywood, furniture, crates, creosoted posts.
Elm	Greedy hedge weed. Far too many in our valleys. Fewer more beautiful.	Nail-tough, boxes, cartwork.

Variety	Soil and Situation	Uses
False Acacia (Robinia)	Dry hot soils.	Valuable everlasting post wood. Spokes, fences, furniture, cart-work, wood nails, much undervalued.
Hornbeam	Cold, frosty, wet soils.	Very hard, wearing parts, pulley blocks, tools.
Oak	Grows quickly on good land. Acorns from biggest trees in close groups make fine stems.	Tough general purpose timber. Even small bits find market as chair parts and wood blocks.
Poplar	In moist land at 15 feet apart.	Valuable for boxes (no taste), fire-proof floorboards, wagon bottoms (no splinters), pulp-wood.
Sweet Chestnut	Light non-limy soils.	Better than oak for beams, fences, poles.
Sycamore and Norway Maple	Very hardy anywhere.	Hardwearing floorboards, dairy utensils, textile rollers.
Walnut	Good, medium lightest soils.	Always valuable timber. Plant orchard style.
Black Walnut	Ditto.	Plant in close groups for valuable timber.
Bat Willow	By water at 15 to 20 feet.	Pegs, hurdles, packing cases, cart boards, baskets, chip baskets, pulp, indoor woodwork.
Larch	Good soil on cold slopes.	Quality long lasting construction timber, posts, fencing.
Japanese Larch	More adaptable to soils.	Rapid windbreak in front of slower permanent. Timber as Larch.
Corsican Pine	Poor dry soils. Quick grower.	Rough construction timber, pit props.
Scots Pine	Poor medium soils.	Rough construction, pit props.
Austrian Pine	Poor and medium soils.	Tough protector windbreak tree.
Spruce, Norway	Soils always moist. Very hardy.	Lissom bending wood, masts, boxes, pulp.
Spruce, Sitka	Rapid, hardy, more adaptable than Norway. Good on swampy ground.	Oars, masts, aeroplane work, pulp. Good windbreak on chalk.
Douglas Fir	Moist sheltered climate.	Not recommended for farm work, probably will be found to be much over-rated.
Apple, Pear, Cherry, Yew	Seedling pears close planted on moist soils soon make timber.	Fine for furniture, cabinet work, musical instruments, turned bowls, etc.

THE CROP ROTATION

I will follow my system of organic surface tillage through a rotation, crop by crop, describing in more detail the methods of soil preparation, seeding and subsequent management of the crop.

The crop which has given rise to more questions about this method than any other, the potato, is in my experience the easiest of all to grow by organic surface tillage, and probably the most spectacular in its results as far as health of crop and saving in labour is concerned. Though it is not one of the major crops in my rotation, in view of the widespread interest and scepticism about the effectiveness of growing it by these methods, I will describe the method of growing potatoes as a part of the root and kale break, in the following rotation:

1st year	Kale—roots—potatoes or arable silage—beans or linseed—10–12 tons an acre of compost.
2nd year	Oats (or wheat)—grazed in early year, then sown with ley.
3rd year	Ley—grazed.
4th year	Ley—mown and grazed.
5th year	Ley—grazed and mown—5 tons an acre compost.
6th year	Ley—grazed and broken for:
7th year	Wheat—grazed in early winter and undersown for autumn and winter grazing.
8th year	Oats (or wheat)—grazed in early year—disced after harvest to encourage weeds for winter grazing.

Soil Preparation. The process of preparation for the potato crop starts immediately the preceding cereal crop is harvested. The field is first of all disced once or twice, according to soil conditions, to germinate weed seeds. It is then left for the winter, and compost may be put on the surface and lightly disced in. But I generally keep all the compost for potatoes until the time of planting.

During the winter there will be a good growth of weeds which may be used for grazing. Though if the land does not readily cover itself quickly with weeds, something is sown in the disced stubble to effect coverage and to provide winter grazing and subsequent green manuring.

Discing to a depth of two or three inches, with the disc harrows at their most acute angle, is the main operation in the spring, and it is started at any time when the soil is sufficiently dry. We like to have a good even tilth by the end of March in readiness for planting in early April. If the soil has not been given ample organic matter in the past, or if the practice has been to plough it down too deep, the topsoil may be so hard and lumpy that the use of the roller is necessary to make an even seed-bed. This was my experience in fields that came more recently under organic treatment.

Planting. The process of planting is extremely simple.

We draw the fixed tine cultivator across the field in the direction we intend our potato rows to run. Some of the tines are removed so that the shallow grooves made by the cultivator tines are at the proper width apart for the potato rows. Eighteen and twenty-four inches apart are usual for early and main crop respectively.

The shallow row is then ready to receive the potatoes, which are planted therein at distances of about a foot apart, for early potatoes, and one foot three inches to one foot six inches for main crop potatoes. We keep our own compost-grown seed each year and select the best tubers for planting. It is customary in orthodox farming to use only the small tubers for seed, but this means that the tubers which have not had the best nutriment are used year after year. It is not possible to improve by selecting the inferior tubers and this partly explains the increasing incidence of disease in the potato crop. As with all other crops use the biggest and the best for seed, and in a few years of organic methods and your own improving seed disease will disappear and yields increase.

The potatoes are covered with compost, just sufficient to give complete coverage to every tuber. Sometimes we go over the plot with a chain harrow drawing a little of the soil into the rows, but when sufficient coverage has been given we merely leave the potatoes with their covering of compost, until there is a good growth of leaf, when we draw the earth around the potatoes in the ordinary way of earthing up.

If no ripe compost is available with which to cover the potatoes, we use any kind of organic manure, but it has been noticeable that the potatoes receiving the less matured manure always give the greatest trouble in weeding. In properly matured compost the weed seeds are killed before it is applied and practically no hoeing is needed.

The most pleasing aspect of this system of potato growing, apart from the freedom from disease and the immense saving in labour at the time of planting, is the ease with which the potatoes are harvested, for though the tubers are well covered with soil they are all at ground level and merely require to be uncovered before picking. This system is bound to improve the efficiency of mechanical lifters, and reduce the number of stones collected by the machines which collect, as well as uncover, the potatoes. (See page 10 for cost comparisons of this method with the orthodox method.)

We get occasional green potatoes by this method but, surprisingly, they have by far the best flavour when baked in a little butter. I always choose the greened potatoes for my own use, though I admit it would not be easy to educate the average consumer to the better flavour, and probable nutritional value, of the green potato grown by my methods.

Kale and Other Crops of the Same Type

Following a seed-bed preparation identical with that for potatoes, the kale seed is drilled, on the flat, during June. A small proportion of the crop is sown in April for early autumn cutting on land which is known to be clean. The reason for the later sowing of the main crop is that ample opportunity is allowed for discing, in order to kill weed seeds which are allowed to germinate on the surface. As all organic matter is on the surface, and this year's application is also applied to the surface and disced in, the kale germinates and grows away quickly, evading the attacks of turnip fly and avoiding the competition of weeds which have all been killed in the earlier cultivations.

Seeding rate is 4 lb. an acre, in drills, or 8 1b. an acre, broadcast, and once sown the crop is not touched, unless weed destruction has not been successful before sowing. No singling is done, and horse or hand hoeing is avoided. The growth of kale by this method is not so stemmy, has a higher proportion of protein and is of a higher feeding value than the coarse thick-stemmed kale which results from earlier sowing and singling.

Beans

Though it is perhaps the best source of protein for farm animals, the field bean is being grown less and less each year because of the many problems to which the crop is subject. Before the days of chemical fertilizers, beans were a traditional and widely grown crop on strong land. In medieval Britain they were one of the most important crops, providing protein for horses and for serfs who could rarely afford meat.

Somerset Farm Institute experimenters came to the conclusion some years ago that the main cause of bean growing troubles, particularly chocolate spot, the most serious disease of beans, was potash deficiency. So plots were laid down with varying quantities of artificial manures and dung, and the potash theory seemed to be confirmed, though the dunged plots were among the best.

In 1946 it was expected that at least it would be possible to proclaim the solution. A heavy dressing, 5 cwt. an acre, of muriate of potash, was applied in the full confidence that this would produce really healthy and abundant yields of beans. But in May of that year when I saw the crop it was almost a complete failure. The only patches that showed any promise were around the headlands, and near an old stack site, where cavings had been burned and spread on the surrounding soil.

It seems then that what the Cannington experiments proved, more than anything else, was the impossibility of growing beans for any number of years *with* artificial fertilizers. What appeared to be a potash problem became worse under heavy applications of inorganic potash, but showed response to organic potash in the form of straw ash.

My own experience indicates that organic manuring in the year of sowing is, however, not the complete answer, though it is an essential to a successful crop.

Some years ago I grew two fields of beans, each of about eight acres. Each had almost identical treatment. One field failed to pod after showing profuse blossom, the other produced a good crop of beans. The explanation of this was in the seed. The field that failed was grown from new seed purchased from seed growers who had reared them with artificial fertilizers. The crop that succeeded was from old seed, bought locally from a farmer who had grown his beans with dung and no artificials. The fact that both fields flowered well, but that only one podded, points to some fault in the fertilization process.

Sir Albert Howard said that he found in his researches in plant breeding that where natural cross pollination of certain plants is prevented, there is a gradual weakening of the ability of the plant to reproduce, and when I discussed my experience of beans with him, he confirmed my suggestion that generations of interference with the natural nutritional process of certain plants by inorganic manuring had an effect on the formation of the flower of the plant and consequently upon its reproductive process. There was in any case no doubt about the weakening reproductive capacity of plants inorganically fed over a number of generations.

In a letter to *The Farmer and Stockbreeder* in 1946, when I had my bean crop experience described above, Sir Albert Howard wrote the following about the growing of beans:

'On all sides one hears that the bean crop is a failure due to the growing inroads of disease—fungus and insect. Why is this? I think I can supply the answer. For the last fifty years I have devoted much time to the study of the bean family, and to the methods of growing leguminous crops for seed, including beans and peas, and have I think rediscovered the secret of success. The crux of seed production in this group of plants is not in finding new varieties, but the provision of the soil conditions these crops most enjoy. The first thing to do is to grow the existing varieties properly, and wait while new types of beans are being bred. The bean like most of our leguminous crops is a mycorrhiza former, that is it exhibits the mycorrhizal association in which microscopic threads (mycelium of certain soil fungi) pass from the humus in the soil into the living cells of the active bean roots to live there for a time in partnership. Eventually these threads, which are very rich in protein, are digested. The digestion products then pass into the sap and so find their way into the green leaves where they are used for the synthesis of more protein. By this natural mechanism—in other words, by this rule in nature—a passage has been provided for protein to move from the humus in the soil into the leaves of the bean. If our farming does not conform with this rule the bean is unable to resist diseases like chocolate spot, or to grow a good crop of seed. Changing the variety, therefore, will not help us, but good farming will. We must add to the soil a substantial dressing of properly made compost or an equivalent volume of first-class muck if we are to get a good crop of beans. Then we shall be working with nature, and all will be well.

'But in growing beans we must avoid the use of artificial manures because these materials would appear to interfere with the digestion of the fungous threads in the bean roots and thereby prevent the leaves of the crop from producing high quality protein for the seed. When this indication is fully confirmed we shall be provided with a simple explanation of the loss of quality which always follows the use of artificials.

'My experience of growing leguminous crops, including beans and peas, for seed during the last fifty years is, of course, not in accordance with the teaching of our Schools of Agriculture, and presumably is not supported by the new Advisory Service. In my student days I was carefully taught that the nodules on the roots of leguminous crops will always take care of the supply of combined nitrogen these plants need, and that the practice of our fathers and grandfathers in always mucking crops like clover was like carrying coals to Newcastle. I gaily set out on a long adventure in research, fortified by these precepts. Practical experience, alas, soon laid them in ruins. Our ancestors were right; the professors were wrong.

'The failure of the bean crop, in the opinion of the pioneers, is the writing on the wall. *Our methods of farming are at fault.* To put matters right four things are needed: (1) we must sweeten our bean land, when this is necessary, by a dressing of ground limestone or chalk at say three tons to the acre; (2) we must shatter the subsoil pan by means of a subsoiler working fourteen to twenty inches below the surface and four feet apart; (3) we must apply a dressing of properly made compost or of good short muck, at the rate of at least twenty tons to the acre, and (4) we must give up the use of artificial manures for beans.'

All my experience of beans was to confirm Sir Albert Howard's views. I studied the habits of my bees in the two fields mentioned above. During the brief spells of weather in which it was possible that season for the bees to work the beans, they showed a distinct preference for the beans bred with dung. No doubt, during a very favourable pollination season, the bees are able to get around to all the flowers which are acceptable to them. In my case the bees preferred the beans grown from naturally raised seed to the beans grown from seed raised by means of artificial manures, though both lots of seed had been sown in the humus-filled soil of my farm, and though all conditions for both fields were otherwise the same.

Soil Preparation. In preparing a field for beans we start immediately after harvest, for early sowing is an essential of successful bean growing.

The stubble is thoroughly disced as soon as the grain is carried off, or should the weather delay harvest, between the stocks or tripods. The ground is left for two or three weeks for weed seeds to germinate, during which time ten tons an acre of compost is spread on the surface. If we are short of compost, raw sewage sludge is carted direct from the sewage works and spread on the surface at the same rate as compost. Sewage sludge contains quickly available nitrogen and beans thrive on it, but it does not last for subsequent crops as long as compost.

The manure is disced into the surface soil but not put under the soil. Especially if sewage sludge is used, it is important that it should remain in the presence of ample air to assist the activity of the organisms needed to break down the manure.

Sowing. The beans are then drilled in rows 22 inches apart, at the rate of $1\frac{1}{2}$ to 2 cwt. an acre, according to condition of seedbed and fertility of the field, or broadcast and disced in.

If you are practising surface cultivation without ploughing, the beans may be sown broadcast and covered with the disc harrows. The need for inter-row hoeing is removed by the system of surface cultivation. Weed seeds have been germinated and killed on the surface before sowing the domestic seed, so there is little if any competition for the bean. The need for sowing in rows, therefore, no longer exists. But if you prefer to sow in rows it can be done by taking some of the tines off the cultivator so that it will draw the soil up into ridges. Then broadcast the seed and afterwards harrow up and down the ridges with a chain harrow or light fixed tooth harrow. There is now also a new bean drill which drops the beans in a channel created by cultivator tines and allows the earth to fall over them afterwards.

Or you may use the old method of ploughing in the beans, so long as the plough is not allowed to go deeper than three or four inches, or just enough to cover the seed.

Linseed

Linseed is one of the easiest crops to grow and one of the most valuable sources of protein for the farm livestock. I have found also that it has great medicinal value, and consider it an important ingredient of the cattle diet, however small the proportion may, through inadequate supplies, have to be.

Some difficulty has been experienced in threshing the crop, particularly after a damp harvest, when the seed may not separate easily from the husk at threshing time or if the crop is not just ripe when cut. But if care is taken to see that the crop is exactly ripe (when the heads rattle together quite noisily and when it is possible to squeeze the head between the fingers and press out ripe light brown seeds) a good threshing machine will make a clean job of linseed.

Soil Preparation. Preparation of the seed bed is the same as for potatoes, except that manuring will not be necessary. If a little compost is available there will of course be no harm in using it, but we rarely do, for we need it more urgently on other crops. Linseed is not a greedy crop and makes only small demands on the soil. It may therefore be grown almost anywhere with reasonable hopes of an economical crop, and no fear of robbing the subsequent crop. But linseed does not itself happily follow another crop of linseed, though of course successive crops of linseed are rarely likely.

Sowing. Seed is drilled in April (early if possible, though it may be delayed until the first week in May if other crops have to be sown), and our rate of seeding has progressively diminished with experience during the past ten years, from 1 cwt. an acre officially recommended, to half that quantity or even less on really good fertile seed-beds. Fifty-six pounds an acre should be ample on well-prepared average soils. We found Royal the most suitable variety, and have used our own seed for the past eight years.

No further attention is given after drilling the crop, unless it is to roll the field, soon after drilling, in order to conserve moisture in a dry spring. But even rolling is an operation which may eventually be dispensed with, as the organic content in the top-soil is increased and water holding, or rather water retaining capacity, is improved, with the increasing sponginess of the soil.

In harvesting linseed we find no special difficulties provided the knife is kept sharp. Experimenting with the binder bed at different levels did show us, however, that the stem of the linseed is less tough some inches from the ground, and much more effective cutting was achieved by raising the bed.

OATS

The only preparation needed for oats, following any one of the first crops in the rotation above described, will be to disc harrow the field twice or three times. Following linseed or potatoes or beans, this may be done in the autumn and a crop of winter oats sown, or following kale it will wait until the spring. In either case the field is quickly prepared and drilled, for it will be in clean friable condition after the kale or potatoes. Though a little weedier after beans or linseed, where compost was used on the seed-bed and left on the surface, the task of working the soil will involve only a few strokes with the disc harrow which will kill all weeds and leave a loose, easily workable seed-bed in which the oats may be drilled.

Some of my best crops have resulted from sowing as little as 1 cwt. an acre where September sowing is possible. The seeding rate is increased $\frac{1}{4}$ cwt. for each month after September up to $1\frac{1}{2}$ cwt.

THE LEY

The ley follows the oats and is either sown under the oats in the spring or on the disced stubble after harvesting the oats.

In established leys I have found the following to be the most important prerequisites of success. Firstly that there should be adequate organic matter in the soil, and secondly that the soil should be sweet, i.e. not lacking calcium.

Clover, like all legumes, is a glutton for organic manures and moisture and it will not grow successfully in an acid soil. I choose then, for the ley, a field that has had a dressing of compost or other organic manure with one of the previous two crops. It need only have been five tons an acre of well-made compost or even less if a green manure crop was worked in with it. This will provide the natural insurance against clover starvation, which often results in soils of low humus content, and also helps the retention of moisture in the critical stages of establishing a ley.

A mixture containing deep-rooting herbs is essential to soil, crop and animal health, assisting in the aeration of the subsoil and the transfer from subsoil to topsoil of important minerals and trace elements.

The mixture I have found successful is as follows in lb. an acre:

*Goosegreen Herbal Ley Mixture**

```
      4 lb.  Perennial Ryegrass (S.23)
      4 lb.  Perennial Ryegrass (S.24)
      5 lb.  Cocksfoot (S.143) ⎫
      5 lb.  Cocksfoot (S.26)  ⎭ on light or medium land
Plus/or 4 lb.  Timothy (S.51) ⎫
      4 lb.  Timothy (S.48)    ⎭ on heavy land
      1 lb.  Rough Stalked Meadow Grass
      1 lb.  Meadow Fescue
      3 lb.  Late Flowering Red Clover (Montgomery or
               Aberystwyth)
      1 lb.  White Clover (S.100)
      1 lb.  Wild White Clover
      2 lb.  Chicory
      4 lb.  Burnet
      ½ lb.  Yarrow
      2 lb.  Sheep's Parsley
      1 lb.  Alsike
      2 lb.  American Sweet Clover
      1 lb.  Kidney Vetch
      2 lb.  Lucerne
      1 lb.  Plantain
      1 lb.  Dandelion
      ½ lb.  Fennel
```

Plus 6 lb. Italian Ryegrass or a bushel of oats if sown direct.

Omit Yarrow or Dandelion if indigenous.

*See Appendix for Suppliers, page 237.

Some plants of comfrey, garlic, raspberry, hazelnut, docks, and cleavers should be provided in the hedgerows if they are not already present.

If we are to sow under the oats, the ley mixture is sown broadcast with a seed-fiddle after the winter oats have been grazed hard to the ground by the cows, or immediately the spring oats have been sown, when a spring-sown oat crop is used as 'nurse' for the ley. Though drilling is often recommended, where there is plenty of organic matter in the surface soil I have never had a failure by broadcasting. If the ground is dry it is sufficient to cover the seed with the roller only. I find a further harrowing unnecessary.

Though spring sowing of grass ley seeds is still the usual practice on most farms, I have in recent years found the ley sown after harvest to be the most successful. The clovers may be slower to establish themselves and some of the shyer herbs somewhat deterred by a first hard winter following so close on their breaking ground; but there is always more certainty of establishment in the autumn because there is always a certainty of ample moisture, the absence of which is perhaps the most common cause of failure after a spring sowing. We merely disc the stubble immediately after the grain is cleared. If there is time to do so and still allow an early September sowing for the ley, we allow a fortnight for the germination of weed seeds and then disc the field again.

The seed is then broadcast on the first calm day. If there is not time to allow weed seed germination, and the field is extremely weedy, we leave it till the spring, using the autumn to allow for stubble cleaning. But we do not hesitate for fear of weeds like dandelion and chickweed, for these are valuable ingredients of the grazing which is to follow, so we encourage them and use them as I describe in my chapter on weeds.

An autumn-sown ley generally provides a much earlier bite in the spring than the spring-sown ley does in its first following spring, for where there is ample organic matter to maintain soil warmth the first flush of young growth continues through the winter, at any rate in the south of England.

Grazed in the first year, this mixture will give a good yield of first-class hay in its second year. The deep-rooters will stand very heavy grazing and indeed to get the best from the ley it should be stocked so that it does not grow away from the cattle in the early summer. If the grass does get ahead of the cattle a cut is taken for silage or the field divided, leaving one or more sections to develop a bulk of growth for silage purposes.

By the fourth year my leys are at their peak and broken at this stage they provide maximum fertility for the succeeding wheat crop.

Wheat

Wheat is the crop which generally follows the ley. Until such time as there is a set of disc harrows available, which will quickly and satisfactorily break a ley without ploughing, this is the only stage in the rotation when I consider ploughing necessary (though there may be occasions when the ground is too wet or too hard and ploughing will more quickly provide soil for working). But the ley should not be ploughed deeply. Four inches, or no more than is needed merely to turn over the turf, should be the maximum depth. Then the turf may subsequently be broken with the disc harrows and chopped up in the top four or five inches of the soil. To plough at a greater depth is only to lose the value of the decaying turf of the ley.

Where we have had time to do the necessary number of discings we have broken leys satisfactorily with the disc harrow and I would consider it the ideal tool for preparing a seed-bed even direct from the ley. The only objection is to the number of times which it is necessary to use the disc harrow in order to get a suitable seed-bed direct from the ley; for this reason only I would advise the plough at this stage in the rotation.

The field is then disced twice or until a satisfactory seed-bed is prepared. It need not be fine so long as the seed is covered, for winter frosts will break down any clods. The wheat is then sown in the months of September and October at the rate of $1\frac{1}{2}$ cwt. an acre. If the soil is rich in organic matter and the date of sowing is September, as little as 1 cwt. of seed is sufficient.

The wheat is grazed hard by the dairy herd in the spring (see 'All-Year-Round Grazing,' Chapter 7) and then drag harrowed. In April or May we then undersow the wheat with 4 to 8 lb. trefoil and 8 to 10 lb. Italian ryegrass, broadcast and rolled in. This provides grazing or green manuring in the autumn and winter, and the trefoil provides by means of its nitrogen-fixing ability additional nitrogen for the wheat.

Wheat is also taken as an alternative to oats, following either beans or linseed, or even oats. Then an opportunity is provided for very early sowing and the provision thereby of earlier spring grazing, or even late autumn grazing. Wheat is really a triple purpose crop and we always sow it with grazing as a deliberate part of its treatment, as well as for the provision of grain for food and straw for bedding and compost making.

Wheat for grain alone has never been a very profitable crop, and many farmers have preferred the more lucrative barley. But managed in the triple-purpose way, and with such immense savings in cultivations as my method effects, I have found it to be one of my most profitable and certainly, after the ley, my most important crop.

After wheat, oats come again in the rotation, but in between the wheat and oats and also after the oats, we take a winter grazing. After the wheat, ryegrass and trefoil, or kale and clover, which are sown under the wheat, or a good crop of weeds will be encouraged after the oats, by immediate after-harvest discing, with the addition if necessary of a seeding of barn sweepings or weed seeds from the thresher, to provide winter weed grazing.

Crops Outside the Rotation

The rotation is not adhered to rigidly. It is merely used as a basis for the cropping plan. The condition of the field, the needs of the livestock and other factors of the moment, make frequent alterations and adaptations necessary. Additionally, some crops such as lucerne are grown on certain fields for a period of seven years, taking that field out of the rotation for that period of time.

If a field is in a particularly high state of fertility, and we may feel that another field which is due for say, a wheat crop, is in need of a recuperative crop, or at least one which does not diminish fertility, then we may take wheat in successive years on the fertile field; but if this is done, undersowing of the second wheat crop with a leguminous mixture for green manuring is never omitted.

A small part of the farm also spends a number of years under market-garden crops, again holding that field out of the farm rotation. It is also found sometimes to be convenient to leave a good ley down for an extra year, or to take a seed crop of some kind, as an extra to the rotation.

Lucerne

I consider lucerne a most valuable farm crop on all types of soil. It is generally advised on thin dry soils, as a provision against drought, but on farms following my methods, problems of drought are very rare, due to the ability of the deep-rooting herbal ley to maintain a good green growth in the most severe drought, and the surface skin of organic matter retaining sufficient moisture to keep cereal and other crops going throughout the longest of summer droughts ever likely to be experienced in the British Isles. But even on soils which do not suffer from drought, lucerne provides an almost continuous source of green food throughout the summer, which may be used for cutting green for cows, for tethering bulls on, as well as for cutting for hay or silage.

My own first piece of lucerne provided an interesting experiment in the subject of nitrogen fixation and usage of leguminous plants. Contrary to orthodox advice, I could not feel the necessity of inoculating any plant with bacterial culture in order to enable it to utilize a natural process. All the orthodox books and experts say that lucerne cannot be grown satisfactorily without soaking the seed in a culture of *bacillus radicicola* which is the organism capable of fixing atmospheric nitrogen in the roots of the plant. I was convinced that the right way around the problem of providing adequate nitrogen for the greedy lucerne, was to see that there was adequate organic nitrogen in the soil. This was done by a heavy dressing of good compost on kale which preceded oats after which the lucerne was sown direct. This ensured that the soil was, by the time the lucerne was sown, rich in organic nitrogen and the organisms of nitrogen fixation. I proceeded in the month of April to sow the lucerne broadcast, and now, in its fourth year, the crop is flourishing and providing a greater bulk of cattle food than any other crop on the farm. Lucerne has never before been grown on the farm as far as we can ascertain. What is more, again contrary to orthodox advice that mowing in the first year will militate against a good establishment of the crop, we grazed the lucerne in early June, mowed it in August, and grazed it again in September—three crops in its first year. And it was up to the knees of the cows again in the last week of February of the second year. So, at any rate on my farm, inoculation was not necessary.

I have two equal sized pieces of lucerne, one sown with 16 lb. lucerne and 3 lb. cocksfoot to the acre, and one with 16 lb. lucerne and 4 lb. timothy. It is too early yet to decide with which grass the lucerne gives the best results. But present indications are that the general advice to use timothy on heavy land and cocksfoot on light land will be confirmed. What I have found is that 4 lb. of timothy was too heavy in my case and threatened to swamp out the lucerne at one stage, but I restored the lucerne by heaving grazing in the early year. The tendency is for a much stronger growth of grass in the early spring, which if not heavily grazed may swamp out the lucerne. This early grazing has proved sufficient to keep the timothy under control. But another time I would sow less timothy, say 2 lb. an acre, or at the most 3 lb., when the balance between lucerne and grass should be maintained without undue need for grazing management of the crop.

Contrary to the established practice of sowing lucerne only on the cleanest land I consider it the best possible cleaning crop. Provided the field is clean enough to get a satisfactory establishment of lucerne, I don't worry about weeds. After two or three times cutting the crop, very few weeds remain, and in its second full year it becomes the cleanest crop on the farm in spite of previous weeds. Lucerne is especially good for eliminating thistles.

We generally graze our first growth in March, mow the second growth in June for tripoded hay, and mow the third growth in August for silage. We often get a further grazing in September or October. Throughout the summer the field is used for tethering bulls, for cutting green food for feeding odd animals, and taking to shows.

I do not consider the lucerne to be an ideal diet on its own. It does not contain a wide enough variety, compared with the herbal ley, and there is, no doubt, a case for the addition of some of the bulkier, quicker-growing herbs, like chicory, in the lucerne mixture. Neither do the cattle show any marked preference for lucerne, against the ley or even a green cereal crop for grazing, which to me is sufficient indication that it is not all a balanced diet should be. But lucerne does provide something green at times when other green food may be scarce, and it does provide an immense bulk of material for use in the winter in conjunction with other foods. What is even more important, its roots grow to a great depth, bringing to the lucerne leaves valuable mineral and trace elements which may not be present adequately in other crops.

Lucerne is also a great labour saver, needing no further attention, once established, for the seven years of its growth, beyond an application of compost whenever it is, and as much as is, available—if possible during the winter of its third and fifth years, though it will always benefit from more frequent applications, being like all legumes a glutton for organic manure.

Green Manuring Crops

COMMON MUSTARD

Mustard is the quickest-growing green manuring plant and therefore the most useful catch crop to be used solely for manurial purposes. Cattle do not favour it for direct consumption so that it cannot serve the dual purpose of cattle grazing or green manuring. Where there is any likelihood of the catch crop being needed for cattle, rape or turnips, trefoil or red clover and Italian ryegrass, or vetches, should be used.

But for purely manurial purposes mustard gives the greatest bulk in the shortest time, and the seed is comparatively cheap.

The mustard is sown immediately after harvest or at any convenient time between two crops. The sooner it can be sown, once the field is bare, the better, for this allows time for the growth of maximum bulk for discing in.

All the preparation needed is once or twice discing to make sufficient soil cover and once over again with the discs after broadcasting 20 1b. an acre of seed.

The crop is disced into the topsoil when in full flower, which on our land now gives a crop of about three feet high. It is never ploughed in, for this puts the mustard where it will do least good—out of reach of the following crop, where, as likely as not, it will putrefy and contribute practically nothing to soil fertility.

RUSSIAN COMFREY

Though I have some experience of wild common comfrey I have never grown the Russian variety, but I believe it has great possibilities as a spare corner crop or on land not in the rotation or around the hedgerows of the organic farm. I am indebted to Mr. Lawrence D. Hills for this information.

As a fodder crop it is on the watery side, 90 percent, and its beta carotene in the fresh state is 77 mg. per kilogramme, compared with the content of average grass of 120 mg. Its dry analysis, taken from a recent sample shredded and put through grass drier, is protein 21.8 percent, fibre 14 percent, ash 13.6 percent, oil 2.1 percent, carbohydrate 37.4 percent, moisture 11.1 percent, beta carotene 122 p.p.m. which compares favourably with much grass meal on the market today. But the colour is poor, and the high moisture content makes it costly in fuel. Its qualities as a silage crop are unknown, but as it will give up to six cuts a year, totalling, according to those who sell it and have sold it for years, 20 to 30 tons in the first year, 40 to 60 in the second, and 60 to 80 in the third, with 120 tons as the target for an acre after that, it is worth consideration and experiment.

As fodder, it is an acquired taste. Cattle learn to like it, some eat it greedily from the start, and it has been used for horses, sheep, goats, pigs and poultry. At New Bells Farm, Haughley, Suffolk, the Soil Association use it for cattle food, and recommend it both as fodder and compost material. The leaves are on the rough side hence the specific name. It is distinct from our native comfrey, *Symphytum officinale,* which is a weed, and useless as fodder, but once they get the taste for the crop stock will leave even grass to eat it. It can be cut from April till November but is deciduous and is no help in winter feeding unless used for silage.

The main reason for its unpopularity is the fact that it cannot be brought in on a normal rotation, it is a long-lived perennial, lasting up to forty years, and it is very hard to kill; the roots have so much depth from which to come up that no method of cultivation will destroy it and the use of sodium chlorate is about the only way to get rid of it.

The place for Russian comfrey is in the odd corner near the compost heap and the farmyard, now growing weeds, where it can be cut quickly for green fodder or compost. It is surprising how little work with scythe and fork will fill a cart to take out to a 'threadbare' field in a dry summer. When it is not required as feed, half an hour with a scythe on an odd Saturday morning will add a ton of material to the compost heap.

The analysis is interesting in the high total of ash, which includes 6.50 percent potash, 2.02 lime, 0.93 phosphates and 0.63 percent manganese apart from trace elements, and of course the larger amounts of these substances locked in the organic matter. It is sappy greenstuff of this type that the economical straw-basis farm compost heap lacks.

The ground should be ploughed and cultivated, if possible getting out as many perennial weed roots as you can, and the crowns planted between March and November three feet apart and three between the rows. It sets seed rarely and is difficult to raise from seed. For the first two years it will need surface hoeing between the rows between cuts. When the plants are established weeds cannot survive under it, and the cut is greatly increased by a mulch of manure or compost.

Experiments have been tried with sawdust mulching between the rows, for the fewer weed seeds that are brought to the surface by hoeing the better. The comfrey will, even in the first year, put on so much growth in three weeks that weeds rarely have a chance to set seed and the hoeing is only to prevent them taking advantage of temporary daylight to flower and seed.

A small patch will enable the organic farmer to try the crop; he has no fear of it spreading, as the roots go down, not outwards like creeping thistle.

The few firms who have the true Russian comfrey, not forms of *Symphytum officinale,* charge about 35s. a hundred (£13 per 1,000 for crowns), but it is so easy to increase that there is no need to buy a further stock. After several cuts have been secured, each plant is a mass of shoots. Either about September or in March, the better season, break off all you need and plant along a furrow, turning the next on to it so they are just covered. Roll and leave to grow. Any gaps can be filled up in showery weather later in the year with further fragments broken off the parents. These should have a growing point and about three or four inches of brown thick root.

In Germany, where Russian comfrey is a favourite smallholder's crop, the custom is to leave the patch down about seven years and then fold pigs on it. The pigs are not rung and eat every bit of root they can scent, after they have cleared the foliage. This is the only way of getting rid of it economically and it enables it to be used as a farm crop like lucerne, outside the normal rotation. The pig 'grazing' system is that described in Chapter 17.

ITALIAN RYEGRASS AND TREFOIL

The combination of Italian ryegrass and trefoil is the obvious choice where there is a likelihood of the catch crop being needed for grazing before it is used for green manuring. We sow 8 lb. of Italian ryegrass an acre and up to 8 lb. of trefoil. This is a heavier seeding of trefoil than is generally recommended but we like plenty and in a summer like 1950 we were grateful for the great bulk of trefoil which grew up in the oats and, when it was obvious that we should never get them dry enough for harvesting in the normal way, we carried the sheaves to the silage pit, cut the bands and packed the mixture of trefoil and unthreshed oats in with a soaking of diluted molasses. This turned out to be really good silage, at least of a quality equal to hay. Without the trefoil the oat sheaves would have been too coarse for silage.

The mixture may be sown with spring oats, or wheat, or separately the day after the oats or wheat are sown; or, under winter oats or wheat after they have been grazed close to the ground in the spring and a little soil loosened with the drag harrows to make a seed bed.

CHAPTER SIX

Making Use of Weeds and Other 'Pests'

WEEDS

At every stage in the rotation we make the fullest possible use of weeds. There was a time when I accepted the orthodox view of weeds as the enemy of the farmer and gardener. But that point of view need now be held only by those who lack the skill to use weeds. There is no better contribution to soil fertility, and the health and abundance of domestic crops, than to allow a thick covering of weeds between crops, and to allow the limited growth of some weeds even in association with the domestic crop.

Nature never leaves the earth uncovered. This is an example which we could follow with benefit in our farming; one which I have found to be the most abundant source of free fertility. The orthodox farmer coming to my farm would probably consider me an untidy farmer. For I have long ago outgrown the desire always to be killing weeds as fast as they appear on my land. The weedless farm is still considered the ideal in orthodox modern farming, and the farmer who allows a dock to exist in the middle of a field is reckoned to be a lazy farmer. But to my mind, the farmer whose destructive instincts are perpetually turned on the weeds of the farm is a wasteful farmer.

The shallow-rooting weeds like chickweed and groundsel contribute great quantities of green manure if allowed to grow to a stage of flowering, provided they are disced in before seeds are set. Further, they achieve a quick coverage of the soil and help to retain moisture at times when a bare soil would dry and crack and allow the sun to destroy the valuable organisms of the surface soil.

Chickweed thrives in the winter when little else will grow, and it forms our main winter green manure, which also contributes to the diet of the cattle during the hungry time of the year. Apart from its nutritional value at a time when little other natural green food is available, it has a medicinal property which makes it almost a crop to cultivate for that reason alone.

Through the winter I carry my young stock on the weed growth of the disced stubble, with the additional food and shelter of a stack of oat or wheat straw harvested from the same field, threshed in the corner of the field, with the straw stacked there for winter consumption. The cattle are allowed to pull away at the straw stack through the winter months, sleep around it at nights, and accumulate dung which is mixed with the small amount of straw which is trampled under foot. When spring comes and the straw is finished we have the makings of a compost heap already partly mixed. The remains of the stack, together with the droppings, are forked up into a heap and allowed to mature through the following summer in readiness for application to the same field in the autumn.

Without these weeds, food would have to be purchased for the outwintering cattle, for even the best pastures will rarely take a large number of cattle through the winter without supplementing with hay. So that the farmer bent on weed destruction at every opportunity, not only has the expense of cultivations necessary to destroy the weeds at intervals throughout the winter, but the cost of purchased food which is necessary to feed the cattle which do not have this free diet of weeds allowed to grow.

Of course we have found that this abundant and quick growth of weeds has only reached the dimensions of an extra free crop since the fertility of the soil has reached a fairly high level. In the early days the growth of weeds during the winter was slight. The time for weeds to flourish was in a drought, and then mainly the deep-rooting weeds which have little grazing value. Chickweed and other bulky soil coverers are attendant upon a high humus content and their winter growth is stimulated by the winter warmth of active soil organisms in a soil rich in organic matter. Poor soils do not have this green coverage, though year-by-year maintenance of the organic matter on top, with additions as often as possible, again to the surface and not ploughed in, quickly builds up the surface skin of spongy material from which good winter growth may be expected.

The deep-rooting perennial weeds on the other hand serve the farmer in a different way. I value the dock and the dandelion, for instance, for their penetration of the subsoil from which they draw minerals which are deposited on the surface, later to be used by the domestic crop. I am sure that all crops grow better in association with others than alone. And to allow a small proportion of docks and dandelions to grow with any cereal or leguminous or root crop, provided the so-called weed does not get the upper hand, brings nothing but benefit to the domestic crop. If there is danger of an excessive seeding of the associated weeds we walk through the field and remove the flowering heads before harvest.

I used to be one of those farmers who are unable to walk through a field without stooping to pull a weed every few yards. My father always carried a walking stick with a 'spud' on the end, with which he would dig out the deep-rooting weed, or at least cut it off below the crown. I proudly imitated this habit, feeling the walking-stick spud was the mark of an efficient farmer. I have since come to realize that it is rather the mark of a thoughtless and unobservant farmer. For when I stopped, before cutting out a dock from my field of wheat, and said to myself, maybe this plant has a purpose, I soon found the answer and withheld the hand of destruction.

What an odd attitude most of us have towards nature or indeed the whole of the universe. If it is not blatantly obvious that a plant or an animal or any other phenomenon of nature has a value to our commercial activities, then we attempt its destruction without further thought. If anything appears in the least way to obstruct, or indeed fail to serve, our artificial activities, our main desire is to be rid of it—to remove it from the face of the earth. It is this flaw in human intelligence which has allowed us to destroy vast areas of fertile land and, in a smaller way on our own British farms, to bring upon ourselves untold pests and diseases which would have remained under the control of nature had we not thoughtlessly destroyed that part of nature whose purpose it was to control the pest or disease. Not only weeds which help to maintain the fertility of our top soil, but all kinds of birds and animals are relentlessly destroyed, because we, in our lack of wisdom, consider that they bear no obvious human benefit.

Mine is the only farm for miles around which harbours a rookery. Mine is the only farm I know where the hare and partridge live in peace, and are not made the objects of mine or anyone else's lust to kill something.

Rabbits are generally considered to be utter and complete vermin, but on British farms at least they have a place in small numbers, and may be taken as an indication that there is waste land on the farm that could be used to some better purpose, or that there are hedges and banks that need to be cleared of undergrowth and ditches that need to be cut back and cleaned. When I first came to Goosegreen the farm was infested with rabbits; but so were the hedges and ditches overgrown and infested with brambles and briars, and Ball Hill was covered with gorse and brambles, providing a perfect cover for the free multiplication of the rabbit colonies. When Ball Hill was cleared and reseeded, and all hedges cut back and ditches cleaned, the rabbits quickly disappeared. For years they were almost non-existent, but gradually returned with the new growth of rubbish along the bank below Ball Hill. As soon as they became brave enough to venture out into my wheat and oat crops for food, I knew it was time I got to work on the hill and hedges and banks again, to remove the excessive cover in which they were once more freely breeding.

It is interesting to note that the preservation of the hare seems to discourage the rabbit. The two species don't seem to hit it off together. And as the rabbits increase the hares become less evident. I do not know the explanation of this, for there does not appear to be any active warfare between them. It is merely that on my farm, at any rate, they do not live happily together.

Foxes which were once troublesome on my farm have com-pletely disappeared since, at the beginning of the war, the hunt ceased in the district.

Let no one think that I am advocating indiscriminate freedom for all wild life, though I am sure this would be the ideal to which to cultivate one's moral courage. I have yet to find a use for the rat, and I must say that I am not hopeful of finding one. I do find it necessary to take meas-ures to keep down the rat population. But here again the simple method of reduction is to take advantage of natural controls. I have found no better means of keeping down rats than keeping up dogs and cats, and above all, allowing no accumulations of rubbish and scrap of the kind in which rats delight to gather.

But what I do advocate is a more thoughtful approach to all natural manifestations. It is wrong to conclude that because there is no clearly apparent human use for a natural phenomenon, it is therefore our duty to destroy it. Destruction is a deadly boomerang. Nowhere is this more apparent than on the farm, in my experience. And of course in this plea for the protection of nature I include bacteria of all kinds. I often think it is man's desire to destroy that creates within him the fear which gives rise to the belief that nature has destructive intentions against man. It is just not true. Nature destroys only the useless and unhealthy, and we serve no permanent good by attempting to preserve what nature has decided should go back to the earth from whence it came. Nature serves the universe in the whole, of which man is an integral part. It is when man stands apart from the universe and regards himself as its lord, that nature finds it necessary to bring him to heel. Let man fit himself into his rightful place, and take no action contrary to nature and the best interests of the universe as a whole, without thought of its consequences even to the least of his fellow-creatures, and he will then know nature to be on his side.

Disc Harrows and Weed Control

The question most often asked in connection with organic surface tillage, and particularly regarding the use of the disc harrow as the main implement of cultivation and seed-bed preparation, relates to the control of weeds. 'Don't you find that the disc harrow spreads docks and couch grass?' and 'How can you keep down weeds without ploughing' are the questions which practically everybody asks when discussing my farming methods.

My advocacy of the use of weeds should not be regarded in any way as an indication that I am happy to practice methods which result in the spread of weeds. It is important therefore that I should say emphatically that organic surface tillage does *not* spread weeds, but rather has the effect of gradually eliminating them and allowing the controlled use of a selected few; that the disc harrow is dangerous only when it is inadequately used.

For reasons which I have elaborated elsewhere in this book, to refrain from ploughing-in weed seeds which have been deposited on the surface soil and to work them lightly into the surface soil where they will germinate and ultimately be destroyed by subsequent cultivations, is the quickest way of achieving the permanent elimination of weeds. Once germinated, everything on the surface may be destroyed, leaving to grow with the crop only the few weeds that may be deposited annually by wind and birds.

A moment's thought by any intelligent farmer will reveal at once that the use of the plough is the surest way of preserving and multiplying weeds. Seeds are placed below the top soil and preserved until the next ploughing when they germinate freely on the surface, often in numbers too great for the good of the domestic crop. Having ploughed down all immediately offending weeds, the average farmer, believing that he need not wait for further weed destruction on the upturned soil, proceeds quickly to prepare a seed-bed which is equally as good for the upturned weed seeds and the sown domestic seed. But the weed seed has been moistened and softened by a year under soil and gets away much more quickly than the sown crop.

Where docks are evident in any numbers, ploughing cuts them up or at least turns up the whole dock plant, which is subsequently cut up by the disc harrow into largish pieces, which are capable of further growth on the seed-bed then prepared. This is where the disc harrow *does* spread weeds such as docks and couch grass. For after ploughing, the disc harrow is rarely used as thoroughly as with surface tillage, and is used on a loose under-soil where the chopping up of dock and couch plants is not thorough enough to achieve complete destruction beyond the power of further growth.

With surface tillage, on the other hand, the crowns of dock plants are thoroughly disintegrated while the plant is still in its growing position, and on a firm base which allows a complete kill. The root of the dock remains in the soil to decay, aerate and feed the soil for the good of the domestic crop. But discing must not be skimped. It is the inadequate use of the disc harrow which spreads weeds and, above all, the inadequate use of the disc harrow after the process of ploughing which exposes whole plants of the kind that will multiply when lightly chopped up.

Where there is a heavy infestation of weeds the only solution is a summer fallow, including the use of the disc harrow and the cultivator. I have seen effective summer fallows on very heavily weed-infested fields with the use of disc harrow only, but the cultivator helps to expose couch grass and other creeping weeds so that they may subsequently be chopped up and baked in the sun. I do not favour the type of summer fallow which seeks to expose a coarse ploughed furrow to bake in the sun. For by this method not only is the furrow baked and the weeds killed, but so are numerous valuable soil organisms—and so is the humus, which loses all its moisture. The repeated use of the disc harrow to destroy weeds that have germinated and been allowed to grow no further than the flowering stage, or the alternate use of cultivator and disc harrow throughout the summer, allowing intervals for the growth of the weeds between workings, is the most effective means of cleaning a badly infested field.

Where a small area of land is being dealt with, and sufficient sawdust is available, nothing is more effective for controlling weeds than a dressing of sawdust to a depth of two to four inches. I tried this on a field of spring oats. When the oats had reached a height of about three inches I spread a strip right across the field with two inches of sawdust. My object was to observe the effect of a top dressing of sawdust on the crop at various stages and at harvest. There was no apparent difference in any respect as far as the crop was concerned. But the absence of weeds in the strip that received the sawdust was remarkable. Many visitors remarked on the sawdusted strip long after there was no sawdust remaining on the ground. Incidentally, it is interesting to note that the sawdust disappeared completely before we finished harvest, and when the field was cleared, the only means of recognizing the strip which had received sawdust was by the absence of weeds in comparison with the rest of the field.

Similarly, dressings of compost, in which all weed seeds have been killed in the compost heap, also has the effect of reducing weeds in a field. Or perhaps it is that the beneficial effect of the compost on the sown crop tends to discourage the weeds by sheer process of competition.

The only permanent means of tackling a field with dock infestation is to pull them by hand. There is no short cut for fields that have been allowed to get out of hand. All short cuts have to be paid for in the long run. Nothing but good farming can achieve good results, and chemical weed killers come not into the category of good farming, but of industrialism and destruction, without good purpose. If weeds are not wanted in a particular field, they can be eliminated in a manner which will make good use of their remains, as a contribution to the humus content of the soil of that field: either by discing them into the surface soil or carting them off and using them in the compost heap. To scorch them out of existence by means of chemicals is merely to evaporate them into thin air, with all else that lives around them. This is where industrialism becomes a blight on humanity, for our resources are limited and we cannot afford to burn them up in this way without paying in some way sooner or later. The way in which we shall have to pay may not be immediately apparent, but we may rest assured that it is certain. For inevitably the boomerang of destruction will operate again.

CHAPTER SEVEN

Grazing Round the Calendar

In seeking to raise the efficiency of milk production by lowering the cost per gallon the tendency is usually to attempt an increase in the yield per cow, often with consequent harm to the health of the cow and the calf she carries during lactation.

A glance at the herd averages of some of the progressively managed dairy herds of the country shows that a reasonable yield limit is being reached if the health of our future cow population is to be valued. But even in the best of herds there is tremendous scope for reduction of the two items which head the costs of every herd, feeding stuffs and labour.

On the average dairy farm feeding stuffs account for about 50 percent, and labour 25 percent, of the total cost of producing each gallon of milk. Before the war the cost per gallon of feeding stuffs was much higher, and labour slightly lower, because of the lower labour demands of purchased feeding stuffs.

But whether we feed home-grown food or purchased compounds, we can reckon that feeding stuffs and labour together take up 75 percent or more of the cost of milk production. And most of the cash expended on these two items is spent in the winter months. During the grazing season these costs dwindle till the dream of every dairy farmer must be continuous summer or, at any rate, continuous grass.

Although it may not be possible to have continuous grass in most parts of the country it is possible, even on heavy land, to have continuous grazing except for the four to six weeks of the wettest part of winter and when snow is on the ground. What is more, the grazing can be of a quality almost equal to grass for ten months of the year or even more on dry light-land farms.

The basis of an all-the-year grazing programme is the ley. The Aberystwyth strains have made it possible to have growth of one or more varieties of grass or clover, in southern England anyhow, from the middle of February to the middle of December, providing the leys are managed so that the right grasses are dominant at the right time.

I have tried several mixtures, with and without the leafy strains and deep-rooting herbs, and while good seasonal grazing can be obtained without them, it is not possible to have a bulky growth of early and late grazing, or a thick well-laid sward to ensure future fertility and strong growth in future years, without a large proportion of herbs and pedigree leafy grasses.

The mixture I have found best suited to dairy grazing contains a basis of S.23 perennial ryegrass, S.26 and S.143 cocksfoot, and S.100 white clover, with the use of Italian ryegrass under certain conditions and where direct re-seeding is necessary on land where it is not possible to take a nurse crop. With the addition of a proportion of New Zealand or commercial perennial ryegrass the dairy farmer has a mixture that will do all he asks of it, provided he asks in an intelligent manner and manages each grass with a knowledge of its capabilities. The addition of the widest possible variety of deep-rooting herbs completes the ideal mixture, of which the mixture on page 49 (see Leys) is the one I have found most successful.

The success of the mixture, in my experience, depends on the proportion of cocksfoot to perennial ryegrass being high enough to prevent the aggressive ryegrass from reducing the cocksfoot to a state of tuftiness. In order to assure the success of the cocksfoot, it should be sown at a rate of not less than 8 lb. an acre and, with perennial ryegrass not exceeding 10 lb. an acre (8 lb. is enough on good land), the result will be an even sward which can be easily managed.

If I sow under winter corn in early April, by the time the corn is harvested I have a good growth of grass which will stand hard grazing right into December. But in recent years I have tended more and more to sow in September on the disced stubble. By this method there is more certainty of moisture immediately after seeding. Most farmers have preferred sheep to graze the ley in the early stages, but I am convinced that the use of sheep is the most certain means of delayed growth in the early spring. The sheep eats too close into the crown of the young plants and makes recovery after the winter rather a struggle for the grasses, which one would expect to see flourishing as soon as spring growing weather comes.

This first grazing then, on my farm, goes either to the dairy herd or to young cattle, depending on the length of growth available.

This, then, starts the autumn grazing season for the dairy herd, when the ley has been spring sown. From the stubble grazing they will go back to the ley in its first full year, which has provided the bulk of grazing throughout the summer.

This I have had divided into three equal parts for rotational grazing. The section which provides the late grazing has been allowed to grow away so that cocksfoot and perennial ryegrass are predominant. If this section is not grazed too bare in the winter the tall grasses are well away again in February and March, when they provide the first grass-grazing of the spring by mid-March. Hard grazing now will correct the balance which was upset in the late summer, when the tall bulky grasses gained predominance.

In the short period when it is too cold to expect any growth on the leys, I plan to have a catch crop of rape and turnips, on to which the cows can be turned for a controlled period each day. If it is too wet for grazing of any kind, the next best thing is first-quality silage made from second-year ley or young oats and vetches, supplemented by thousand-headed kale, which is leafier and higher in protein content than the marrow-stem kale. The kale can usually be grazed with practically no waste if the grazing periods are controlled.

I make a point of having at least one field of September-sown winter oats or wheat in one of the driest fields on the farm, which, without any top dressing if previous management has fixed adequate atmospheric nitrogen, should give grass equivalent grazing by the third week in February.

The earlier the oats or wheat is drilled in the summer the earlier it will be ready for grazing, and in a dry late autumn will often give good grazing at a lean time, as well as again in the spring, with nothing but benefit to the subsequent corn crop. One year my cows were grazing Picton oats, sown the third week in September, by the third week in February.

The lodging of cereal crops has become one of the most difficult problems on the farm. Yet though our average yield is far higher than the rest of the county (wheat 30 to 40 cwt. an acre, oats also 30 to 40 cwt. an acre), we never have a laid crop. Grazing is a sure preventive where otherwise organic methods are practised. Of course, a straw weakened by excessive nitrogenous manuring will probably lodge anyhow.

Early-sown winter oats and vetches, and late spring-sown oats and vetches, in addition to the lucerne, provide a high-quality reserve of grazing for almost any time of the year, should anything go wrong with the management of the ley or corn grazing. In addition, these vetch crops are a first-rate source of silage and 'in-between' grazing for the emergencies which are bound to arise.

To summarize, my grazing programme is as follows:

Grazing	Crop	Sown
Early December	New leys	April or September
Late December and January	Turnip greens and rape, kale	Kale, March-June Turnip and rape, July-September
February and Early March	Winter oats and wheat	September
March	2nd year leys—after shut for hay	On section managed for top grass predominance in previous summer
April-September	1st and 3rd year leys. (Oats and vetches or lucerne in reserve for drought or bad ley management)	Rotationally limited (September or April and May)
September	Stubble grazing (Italian rye and trefoil)	April-May
October	1st and 3rd year leys and lucerne controlled	Rotationally
November	New leys or stubbles	April

This programme, linked with a cropping rotation that provides a maximum of home-grown feeding stuffs, has reduced my labour and feeding stuffs cost to a low level. And made me a far happier man than I was when I had two men carrying food to the cows most of the day for three or four months of the year.

CHAPTER EIGHT

The Ley on the Fertility Farm — Costs and Returns

W hen I first started to clear the scrub on Ball Hill, ready to re-
seed it, the local pundits were extremely sceptical, though,
I fancy, a little curious. It had never been more than a rabbit
run before, and even the rabbits had to move down the hill to find food.
The soil is shallow and the slope is such that a crawler tractor could
only plough it one way, and that with some trepidation on the part of
the driver.

My neighbour said, 'It's all very nice as a piece of spectacular work,
but it won't pay you.' I did not think I should lose anything on it and,
in any case, I could not make the hill any worse than it was. I had been
costing my leys lower down the hill and knew that if I could get a
'take' I should not be out of pocket.

The County Agricultural Committee was at that time quoting £10 an
acre for average re-seeding work, and in the minds of many farmers
even this price seemed too high when set against estimated returns. I
could not get a quotation for Ball Hill, which meant that the cost was
likely to be in excess of a price which was considered by many to be
prohibitive.

Neither the County Agricultural Committee nor the various other
advocates of ley farming have yet been able to provide figures, derived
from farm costings, to show convincingly that the re-seeding of some
of our *best* pastures is a profitable proposition. The best that has been
offered in the way of encouragement is the vague promise of two or
three times the grazing capacity, depending on the quality of the land
re-seeded.

But the man who considers his present pastures good is not going to rip up his good old grass, spend £10 to £15 an acre on re-seeding it, and run the risk of an unsuccessful take, merely on the strength of an uncertain prospect of doubled grazing capacity. He will prefer the certain grazing for half the stock and resort to the nitrogen bag for a temporary increase in stocking capacity—unless he is convinced in actual demonstration—backed by evidence of solid returns under ordinary farming conditions.

Failing authentic details of this kind I tried to produce them for myself, and have found that the claims made for leys, which have been guesses in most cases, are extremely modest when compared with the costed returns from well-managed leys.

The Dairy Farmer is now sponsoring a most valuable grassland recording scheme which will do more than all past expert advocacy to demonstrate the value of the ley and to grassland ulitisation.

Ball Hill cost me over £12 an acre. I had no cash crop to take in the first year, yet it paid the full cost and a profit in grazing value in twelve months from the time of seeding. And this was from store cattle only. The returns from milking cows would no doubt have been much more.

The six acres provided me with 304 heifer-weeks of grazing during the first twelve months from seeding. At a charge of 5s. per head per week, which is reasonable considering the high quality of the grazing and the grand condition in which the heifers were maintained, the repayment on my outlay of £74 17s. 11d. was £76.

This return was purely from heifer and in-calf cow grazing. No account was taken of milk returns on two occasions when the cows were turned in to help control the growth. This means, then, that my ley was paid for in its first year, leaving me with grazing of a quality equal to the best in the district in place of a useless scrubby sheep-run that would not support a buck rabbit before. The re-seeding was done in 1943, and will be repeated in 1951, so that the cost spreads over eight years.

An example of the ley as a milk producer was another field—Underhill Close. Underhill Close grazed milk cows entirely—again, except for a period when growth was beyond control and a cut of hay was taken.

The seed was broadcast on Underhill Close in April, under Desprez 80 winter wheat, which had been grazed down bare with cows. The grazing enabled the seeds to get a good start without harming the subsequent wheat crop. Cost of manure was £2 an acre, seed £4 5s., labour and power 8s. an acre; a total seeding cost of £6 13s. an acre. Added to this was 5s. an acre for fencing materials, made necessary by the dividing of the field for rotational grazing.

Against a total cost of £6 18s. an acre, there was an income from milk of £59 an acre during the months April to October.

When the cost of feeding stuffs, £91 13s., fed in addition to the grass, are deducted from the gross milk income of £715 1s. 7d., from the cows which grazed exclusively on this field, there is a clear net return of over £50 an acre. In addition, four tons of hay were taken from the field at a time when the grass grew away from the cows.

It is clear beyond doubt from these figures that good leys pay well, both as grazing for young stock and for milking cows. While the visible profit is the greater when milk cows are the agents of conversion, the foundation of sound health which young stock undoubtedly gain from ley grazing, probably raises the lower cash returns of this class of grazing to a level of equal value with dairy cow leys.

But if, by cheap mixtures and stinted cultivations, the attempt is made to keep down costs, ley farming will soon land the most affluent farmer in queer street. The best obtainable mixture for the class of land, carefully sown in well-cultivated land which has previously been well farmed, followed by intelligent management, will more than repay the cost of the three- or four-year ley every year of its life.

An example of the simple system of costing which I use for my leys may help to dispel any doubts regarding the value of re-seeding. Extracts from my field record book on the next six pages refer to the two fields, Ball Hill (or Sheeps Sleight on Ball Hill) and Underhill Close (see map, page 234) in the years 1943-45.

COSTS AND RETURNS

SHEEP'S SLEIGHT on BALL HILL, 6 acres.　CROP, re-seeded to ley.

Date	Operation	Labour (Name and Hourly Rate)	Power (at Per Hour)	Time (Hours)	Materials	Cost £ s. d.	Income £ s. d.
1943 May	Clearing scrub	A.D. 1/6	Hand	24		4 6 0	
		J.B. 1/3	do.	20			
		G.E. 1/3	do.	20			
	Pre-discing	J.B 1/3	Tractor at 2/6 an hour	35		6 11 3	
May 30	Ploughing	W.A.C Contract	Crawler			7 10 0	
July	Discing and rolling	W.A.C Contract	Crawler			5 0 0	
	Water trough and tapping main	R.D.C				4 0 0	
1944 March	Second ploughing	W.A.C	do.			7 10 0	
April	Discing and rolling	do.	do.			5 0 0	
	Manuring	do.	do.		6 tons grd. limestone	4 12 6	
					Compost	7 19 2	
	Labour, etc.	do.	do.			4 0 0	
May 6	Broadcasting seed	A.D. 1/6	Hand fiddle	6	30 lb.	0 9 0	
May 1944 to May 1945	Grazing 304 heifer-weeks at 5/- (Details from diary)				At £3 p.a.	18 0 0	
					Total cost:	£74 17 11	1st year Income: £76 0 0

COSTS AND RETURNS

SHEEP'S SLEIGHT on BALL HILL, 6 acres.   CROP, re-seeded to ley. (Adjusted for inflation, 2006*)

Date	Operation	Labour (Name and Hourly Rate)	Power (at Per Hour)	Time (Hours)	Materials	Cost £	Income £
1943 May	Clearing scrub	A.D. 1/6	Hand	24			
		J.B. 1/3	do.	20			
		G.E. 1/3	do.	20			
	Pre-discing	J.B 1/3	Tractor at 2/6 an hour			139	
May 30	Ploughing		Crawler	35		212	
July	Discing and rolling	W.A.C Contract	Crawler			242	
	Water trough and tapping main	W.A.C. Contract				161	
		R.D.C				129	
1944 March	Second ploughing	W.A.C	do.			237	
April	Discing and rolling	do.	do.			158	
	Manuring	do.	do.		6 tons grd. limestone	146	
					Compost	251	
	Labour, etc.	do.	do.			126	
May 6	Broadcasting seed	A.D. 1/6	Hand fiddle	6	30 1b.	6	
May 1944 to May 1945	Grazing 304 heifer-weeks at 5/- (Details from diary)				At £3 p.a.	568	
						Total co st: £2,374.48	1st year Income: £2,399.08

*Editor's note: The author's historic financial data was converted to modern currencies and approximately adjusted for inflation, using the consumer price index. This most certainly will not correlate to modern costs and prices, but should be utilized for general directional trends only.

COSTS AND RETURNS

SHEEP'S SLEIGHT on BALL HILL, 6 acres.   CROP, re-seeded to ley. (Adjusted for inflation, 2006*)

Date	Operation	Labour (Name and Hourly Rate)	Power (at Per Hour)	Time (Hours)	Materials	Cost $	Income $
1943 May	Clearing scrub	A.D. 1/6	Hand	24		255	
		J.B. 1/3	do.	20			
		G.E. 1/3	do.	20			
	Pre-discing	J.B 1/3	Tractor at 2/6 an hour	35		389	
May 30	Ploughing	W.A.C Contract	Crawler			445	
July	Discing and rolling	W.A.C. Contract	Crawler			297	
	Water trough and tapping main	R.D.C				237	
1944 March	Second ploughing	W.A.C	do.			436	
April	Discing and rolling	do.	do.			290	
	Manuring	do.	do.		6 tons grd. limestone	269	
						462	
					Compost	232	
	Labour, etc.	do.	do.				
May 6	Broadcasting seed	A.D. 1/6	Hand fiddle	6	30 1b.	12	
May 1944 to May 1945	Grazing 304 heifer-weeks at 5/- (Details from diary)				At £3 p.a.	1,045	
						Total co st:	1st year Income: $4,414
						$4,369	

*Editor's note: The author's historic financial data was converted to modern currencies and approximately adjusted for inflation, using the consumer price index. This most certainly will not correlate to modern costs and prices, but should be utilized for general directional trends only.

UNDERHILL CLOSE, 12 acres.

CROP, 3 years ley sown under winter wheat (Desprez 80)

Date	Operation	Labour (Name and Hourly Rate)	Power (at Per Hour)	Time (Hours)	Materials	Cost £ s. d.	Income from Milk—1944 £ s. d.
1942 November	Manuring	A.D. 1/6	Tractor 2/6	10	Manure	2 0 0 24 0 0	April 119 17 4 May 89 19 5
1943 April	Broadcasting seed	A.D. 1/6	Hand	8	36 lb. seed p.a. at 85/-	0 12 0 51 0 0	June 88 16 8 July 89 3 4 Aug. 110 2 6
April	Dragging	Man 1/6	Tractor 2/6	6		1 4 0	Sept. 96 13 8
1944 March	Fencing	2 men at 2/6	Hand	8	Wire £3	1 0 0 3 0 0	Oct. 120 8 8
	Total cost of making ley					£82 16 0	
	Total Income						715 1 7
	Less feeding stuffs						91 13 0
	Nett Income						£623 8 7

UNDERHILL CLOSE, 12 acres.

CROP, 3 years ley sown under winter wheat (Desprez 80). (Adjusted for inflation, 2006*)

Date	Operation	Labour (Name and Hourly Rate)	Power (at Per Hour)	Time (Hours)	Materials	Cost £	Income from Milk—1944	£
1942 November	Manuring	A.D. 1/6	Tractor 2/6	10	Manure	66.81	April	3,783.82
						801.75	May	2,840.1
1943 April	Broadcasting seed	A.D. 1/6	Hand	8	36 lb. seed p.a. at 85 /-	19.34	June	2,804.19
						1643.76	July	2,814.71
April	Dragging	Man 1/6	Tractor 2/6	6		38.68	Aug.	3,476.3
							Sept.	3,051.99
1944 March	Fencing	2 men at 2/6	Hand	8	Wire £3	31.57	Oct.	3,801.7
						94.7		
			Total cost of making ley			£ 2664.93		22,572.81
			Total Incomew					2,893.1
			Less feeding stuffs					
			Nett Income					£ 19,679.71

*Editor's note: The author's historic financial data was converted to modern currencies and approximately adjusted for inflation, using the consumer price index. This most certainly will not correlate to modern costs and prices, but should be utilized for general directional trends only.

UNDERHILL CLOSE, 12 acres.
CROP, 3 years ley sown under winter wheat (Desprez 80) (Adjusted for inflation, 2006*)

Date	Operation	Labour (Name and Hourly Rate)	Power (at Per Hour)	Time (Hours)	Materials	Cost $	Income from Milk—1944 $
1942 November	Manuring	A.D. 1/6	Tractor 2/6	10	Manure	122.93	April $6,962.23
1943 April	Broadcasting seed	A.D. 1/6	Hand	8		1,475.22	May $5,225.78
					36 lb. seed p.a. at 85/-	35.59	June $5,159.54
April	Dragging	Man 1/6	Tractor 2/6	6		3,024.52	July $5,179.06
						71.17	Aug. $6,396.39
1944 March	Fencing	2 men at 2/6	Hand	8	Wire £3	58.09	Sept. $5,615.66
						174.25	Oct. $6,995.13
			Total cost of making ley			$4,903.47	
			Total Income				$41,533.79
			Less feeding stuffs				$5,323.30
			Nett Income				$36,210.67

*Editor's note: The author's historic financial data was converted to modern currencies and approximately adjusted for inflation, using the consumer price index. This most certainly will not correlate to modern costs and prices, but should be utilized for general directional trends only.

CHAPTER NINE

Managing the Ley

I was brought up on temporary leys in the north of England and, as with all farming practice, acquired certain set ideas from my father. But the more I grow leys, and the more I vary my methods of managing them, the more I learn that there is more to be learned than the experts themselves have yet learned.

Each new ley convinces me more firmly that there can be no rule-of-thumb management of temporary grass. It is as impossible for me to prescribe for your ley as it is for a monkey to prescribe for a polecat. Every farmer is a different animal when it comes to the management of leys. What is right for me may land you in disaster, and vice versa.

My father taught me twenty-five years ago never to mow in the first year of a ley of longer than one year duration. My Professor of Agriculture confirmed the same advice and my County Agricultural Organizer underlined it.

My own experience has shown that while this advice is safe, like many safe policies, it is not always the most profitable. Indeed, in my opinion, it is not possible to get the best out of ley farming, if this rule is observed to the letter, year in, year out.

All sorts of factors contribute to a decision whether or not to mow in the first year. The only man who can make the right decision is the man who lives with the ley; the man who has nursed it from birth knows the soil and the previous management of the field and the behaviour of the particular ingredients of the mixture used on that particular field.

What is more, if two men reached the same decision to mow a field of temporary grass in its first year, and tossed a coin to decide who should manage or perform the operations on the field, the result might be twice as productive with one man as with the other, even discounting the use of fertilizers.

Six years ago I laid down a field with a three-year ley and divided it into three portions. One was to be grazed every year; the other mown

78

in its first year, and the third mown with its first crop and a seed crop taken from its second.

The third portion did not go exactly to plan, for just before the seed heads of the clover were ripe we became short of keep and the cows were turned in. This third portion, then, had what some would regard as the worst possible management, the first crop being mown and the aftermath allowed to go to seed.

The other two sections were carefully managed so that in the first section the treatment was orthodox and very correct, i.e. first-year grazing right through, and the second section the treatment was what the experts would regard as bad, i.e. first crop mown, second crop grazed.

Of the three types of treatment the second was the most productive, though only a fraction ahead of the first section, which in turn was little ahead of the third section. What is significant is that the whole field finished up a good level ley, and so far as establishment of the ley was concerned each treatment produced virtually the same results. Each portion went into its second year, a first-class ley. It was impossible to distinguish one section from the other with the dividing fences removed.

What made it possible to establish a good ley in spite of my disregard of all the best advice against first-year mowing?

The answer, in my opinion, is primarily in the management of the autumn and winter of the sowing year. This is *the* vital period in the establishment of a spring-sown three- or four-year ley, and it is at this stage that all the rules must be regarded and all one's knowledge of the behaviour of the different grasses and the different fields must be brought to bear.

The first essential is, of course, to observe the condition of the ley at the time of cutting the corn if the ley was spring sown. In the field I have quoted, at the time of corn cutting, grasses were very thin and clover almost non-existent. Normally, it would not have been considered fit to leave, and the cultivator would have gone in between the stooks as the binder came out of the field, but weather conditions prevented this and thereby gave the ley a chance.

By the time the corn was carried it was possible to quote the old maxim: 'A plant a stride, let 'un bide'—but only just. At this kind of crisis in the establishment of a ley it is my experience that it will stand and benefit from the heavy grazing of light-footed heifers such as Jerseys, but will be ruined by the deep-biting noses of the sheep.

The heifers give the necessary encouragement to the plants that are too nervous to show themselves, whereas the sheep bite the very hearts out of the few plants that have ventured above ground.

On this particular ley hard grazing by heifers worked magic and the field was soon an even mat of clover, with the grasses just evident, but only just. This is the condition which the end of December should see on the ley that may be mown in its first year. The grasses will then get going in the spring for an early cut of grass, and the clovers are strong enough to stand a good cut of red clover before the white clover is advanced enough to be damaged.

A rest after the first hay crop will see the white clovers flourishing again among the grasses that were allowed to get the upper hand in the hay crop. Hard heifer grazing again will even the balance of the mixture, and after a further rest the stage is set for the long, strong tongue of the milking cow.

It is quite amazing what bad management a ley will tolerate once a sound and balanced establishment has been achieved in the first few months. If things do go wrong in subsequent months, the quickest remedy is a topping with the mower. Get things right back to the ground and start again. With controlled grazing, then, it is surprising what new life can be brought to a ley which was dying from cruel treatment.

If the first grazing has been heavy, and continuous rather than 'on and off,' there is one winter operation which, if neglected, may make a ley grazed in its first year finish the year in a much worse condition than the ley which is mown in its first year. That is dung-spreading.

Careful spreading of the dung-spots before the ley is left for the winter rest will ensure an even growth in the spring. If the task is omitted, or inadequately done, the ley will grow patchy and a large proportion of the grazing will become sour and coarse. Give the cows a choice of the aftermath of a mown ley, or the aftermath of a grazed ley rank with unspread dung-spots, and they will choose to follow the mower every time.

In my opinion, then, the dangers of grazing in the first year are as great, if not greater, than those of first-year mowing.

But a good ley farmer, with the right kind of stock and a sharp mower knife, should be able to make an equally good ley either entirely by mowing or entirely by grazing or, better still, by a deft combination of the two.

No crop pays better than grass for winter and early spring attention. Once the year has turned, no opportunity should be lost to begin what,

3a. Ley Management. Rank growth around unspread dung.

3b. Goosegreen herbal ley (third winter). Ingredients identifiable on this photograph: chicory, plantain, sheep's parsley, alsike, white clover, lucerne, timothy and ryegrass. Photograph taken February 6th 1951.

4. Spreading dung droppings on the ley. A job for the farmer's son.

on the best-managed farms, are the first cultivations of the season. Indeed, preparations for early bite would have been best begun before the first winter frosts.

I find that by careful planning the influence of winter on the subsequent success of a ley can be considerable.

Firstly, the ley which is to be broken up in the following summer is the one to carry the stock through the winter, particularly on heavy land such as mine. If plenty of straw is used, this practice serves three ends:

1. A heavy dressing of dung.
2. Easy utilization of straw.
3. The preservation of the younger leys for early spring bite.

The weight of winter stocking on the second- or third-year ley is not the serious problem it would be on the younger leys that are needed in good condition for later years. In fact, the heavier the stocking the better the results, providing straw is used lavishly.

The wetter the land, and the heavier the stocking, the more effective is the dressing of the trodden straw-and-dung compost. For plenty of straw is needed to keep the stock reasonably dry and comfortable, and the softer the land the better the treading of straw.

The straw serves three purposes. It provides food for the stock; it mixes with the dung to add potash and phosphates to the surface soil already rich in nitrogen fixed by the clover in the ley; and on heavy land it increases the humus content, and thereby lightens and improves the friability of difficult working fields.

With this method of pre-breaking livestock cultivation of leys, it is advisable to omit ploughing when the time comes to break the ley in the following summer and merely go into it with the heavy disc harrow. The saving in time will make it possible to drill very early wheat, which will come for spring, or even autumn, grazing.

The younger leys have the dung droppings spread as evenly and thinly as possible soon after the stock leaves the field in the autumn. If dung is left where it is dropped the winter and spring rains drive concentrated liquid manure into the soil and cause rank growth which even a starving animal hesitates to eat.

As soon as it is possible to get on the land with horses or tractor a thorough chain-harrowing is given. If I have the courage I use the light drags. It may seem drastic, but grass pays for drastic treatment, both in cultivations and in grazing.

I never use top dressings or artificial fertilizers; indeed, my difficulty is to keep pace with the growth when it starts, on a field that has been previously properly farmed. In my experience, a far more effective way of obtaining early growth (which, after all, is more essential than the temporary increase of bulk growth on a ley), of a quality far superior to that gained by artificial fertilizers, is to blanket the ley with an even covering of straw.

An important aspect of 'early bite,' which is forced by nitrogenous chemical fertilizers, is that though the quick soft growth of grass appears to be in every way similar to midsummer grass it in no way compares in feeding value. It is easy to force bulk growth by nitrogenous fertilizers, but in my experience the cost is not justified in returns, and the subsequent slower growth which always follows the first results of earlier stimulation.

My method is to give a good covering of straw, yet not enough to smother the grass. It is worth while to spread the straw carefully, evenly, and in a quantity that will allow the young plants to grow through the straw in the spring. The straw is then left to rot on the ground. The covering of leys with straw in the winter protects the grasses and clovers from frost and maintains warmth in the topsoil, encouraging bacterial activity where it is most needed and at a time when it is usually lacking.

The effect of this is to provide ideal conditions of temperature and nutriment for the young plants long before they would be available on leys that receive no winter attention or receive only the orthodox spring top dressing.

The value of strawing leys was first made clear to me many years ago when I carted out a surplus of straw to be picked over by some cattle wintering out. A severe winter made me bring the cattle into yards before the straw was eaten. It was therefore spread evenly over the grass to avoid damage beneath the heaps of straw.

No further thought was given to the matter until the time came to give a top dressing in the early year, and it was found that on the section of the field covered with straw growth was already under way. This part therefore received no manures, while the unstrawed section had 1 cwt. nitro-chalk and 2 cwt. superphosphate per acre.

I was surprised to find that the unmanured straw section was fit to graze two weeks before the manured part and, what is more, recovery after the first grazing was noticeably quicker on the part that was strawed. The only explanation I can give to this is the difference in soil

84

temperature brought about either by the straw raising the temperature of the strawed section or the chemical manures lowering the temperature on the other section.

It seems clear, then, that where there is ample straw which cannot be used elsewhere it is well to give some time to spreading it on grass that is needed for early bite. The market gardener uses glass cloches to warm his soil and protect his valuable crops during the winter and spring. For the farmer, glass coverings are too costly. But straw is cheap, and it is a crime to burn it. If it pays the market gardener to cloche his crops, it will pay the farmer likewise to straw the most valuable of his crops—grass.

CHAPTER TEN

'Yard-and-Parlour' Milking and Compost

T he system of wintering and milking the cattle may be regarded as the pivot of the whole system of manuring the farm, and incidentally to the freedom of the cattle themselves, which is essential to their health.

I have operated what is known as the 'Yard-and-Parlour' system since early 1943, and I am satisfied that it is the most economical of labour both in the work of managing and milking the cattle and in utilization of manure.

All except the milking herd and the smallest calves spend the whole of their time out of doors, and the cows themselves are out until Christmas, or even longer if the weather is not extremely cold. The cows are allowed all possible freedom, and are never tied by the neck, except when young to teach them to be controlled by halter. But we have to bring them in for a part of the winter, for the sole purpose of accumulating manure for incorporation with other vegetable wastes of the farm for compost.

At milking time the cows are moved to an assembly yard, where they await the milking process, in full view of the milking parlour, which has an open back. This open-backed milking parlour is important (though it may not always be pleasant in the northern winter), for the waiting cows witness all the operations of milking and production ration feeding, which excites them to give down the milk immediately on entry to the milking parlour.

The cows stand for milking in batches of six or eight. One man can manage six good cows at a time with three milking machine units, though assistance is needed when four units are in use. The operator gives production ration to the first cow, cleans her flanks, washes and massages her udder, draws the foremilk, and attaches the machine at once. Warm water is the most effective for massaging and is readily available where the boiler is used daily. The third and fifth cows are followed in succession.

The performance is then repeated on the second cow, by which time the first cow is ready to have the last drops of milk expelled from the udder by dry-hand massage. This is done by grasping the udder above the teat between the thumb and fingers and with two hands stroking downwards vigorously, first one and then the other side of the udder.

No time is wasted in dipping teat cups between cows, as this has been found to be unnecessary. See Mastitis, Chapter 20. The unit is detached and the milk released from the recording jar after the yield has been recorded (this I consider essential at every milking for accurate records and proper management, weekly weighings are not true records). The second cow is then attached at once, and the process continued down the line.

The cows pass out at the front of the milking parlour and return to the yard or the field.

Cows are arranged in order of milking, according to the quantity of milk given and length of time needed to be milked, to minimize as far as possible uneven periods between cows.

Cows which give their milk quicker than they are able to eat their food are afterwards given an additional production ration. As far as accommodation permits, the very best producers are given a separate house for special feeding treatment, at least during winter nights, though this is very rare, for it is far more economical to have a herd of level milkers—needing no extra, special feeding—all managed on a purely commercial scale with the minimum of labour.

When cows are spending their nights in the yard they move from the dispersal yard, after milking, to the night yards, of which we have three, each holding twelve to fifteen cows. We divide them according to yield, so that all the recent calvers go together, and all the cows which are nearing the end of their lactation go together. Newly calved heifers are given a third yard, so that before going in yards with the older cows they get accustomed to their new companions in the fields. Cows are not, as yet, dehorned and we have no trouble which justifies the removal of horns or the work of dehorning them as calves. I still feel that the need for dehorning is an indication of the lack of care in managing the young stock and subsequent handling and arranging in yards, according to the individual temperaments of the cows. We do give some attention to the training of the horns of the heifers if they show signs of growing outwards too wide. The turned-in 'crumpled' horn is the fashionable and attractive style for Jerseys, and horns trained in this way are safe. Labour and accommodation difficulties do, however, make an extremely strong case for calfhood dehorning which is painless.

Each day we cart into the yards ample clean wheat straw for bedding; and, so that there is some pre-mixing of the ingredients before the manure goes to the compost heap, we also spread a small proportion of sawdust, ground limestone and soil, as convenience allows. At the start of the winter the bottom of the yard is covered to a depth of a foot or more with sawdust, which soaks up any liquid manure which may find its way to the bottom of the yard. The yards are also drained to liquid manure tanks, from which we may collect any further surplus liquid which may soak through the bedding and the sawdust. The yards are open to the sky, which I consider beneficial to the manure (as well as the health of the cattle), which receives a necessary proportion of moisture, and thus obviates the need to water the compost heap later. Indeed, one of our 'yards' is nothing more than a kraal fenced off from the corner of the orchard, with the shelter of the wall of a building on one side. Shelter from above is not necessary for the cows, as I quickly discovered from yarding cows in a yard which provided some shedding along one side. Except in the fiercest thunder-storms, when rain beat down unmercifully, the cows preferred to sit out with the open sky above them. With this demonstration of the cow's own choice, and the added value of rain-moistened manure, I gave up all ideas of having my yards covered.

The power of the animal body to retain heat, even in the most extreme frosts, is demonstrated by the icicles which are to be found on the hair of the cow's back, eyes and nose, during frosty weather. If there were any considerable loss of heat from the body during cold weather, then the heat would melt any frost which was on the hair of the cow.

The manure is allowed to accumulate in the yards throughout the winter and similarly in any loose boxes in which calves and calving cows are housed. So long as clean straw is spread each day, so that the animal has a perfectly clean bed on which to lie, the dung below adds comfort and warmth to the animal. The hard labour of daily 'mucking out' is avoided and the only portion of the cattle sheds which has to be cleaned is the milking parlour, which is no more than the width of eight cows. As the cows pass through quickly we generally manage each milking time without any dung being made in the parlour itself. A swill down with the cold-water hose after milking quickly cleans and freshens the floor of the milking parlour in readiness for the next milking.

5a. The milking parlour at Goosegreen.

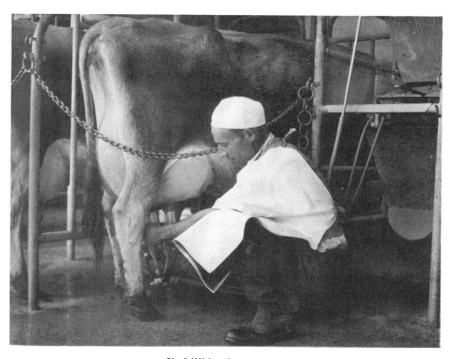

5b. Milking in progress.

6a. Materials for compost—hedge trimmings, straw, old sacks, etc.

6b. Farmyard manure for compost—finished heaps in background.

When the spring sowing is done, and the cows and young stock are all out at grass—in other words, when there is little other productive work to be done—we make a large-scale attack on the manure in the yards and sheds. This is carted out with tractor trailer and horse cart to the site of the compost heaps, and compost is made as we clean out the yards.

We have previously, at various times during the winter and spring, collected and deposited at the site of the compost heaps any material to be used in the heaps, such as hedge trimmings, old sacks, threshing cavings, straw, weeds, including couch grass, docks and thistles, kale and cabbage stumps, sawdust, yard scrapings, mud and soil, ditch cleanings and anything of organic origin which may be found on or around the farm.

As far as possible, we site the compost heaps in the field to which the compost is subsequently to be applied, and if we have been able to thresh the previous crop in the field, then we have a rick of straw to be used in the compost, or the remains of a rick of straw which the outwintering young stock may have had for winter rations and shelter. It is convenient to this straw-stack site that the heap is made, generally in a corner of the field which will interfere as little as possible with the sowing of the crop. Most fields have an awkward corner which will serve this purpose.

In addition, we also have a large site for compost heaps near the farm buildings, for though the main activity in compost making takes place in the spring and autumn, there are many times during the year when we have time to build a small heap, and this necessitates a convenient site close at hand so that the work may proceed quickly between other operations on the farm.

How to make Compost without Turning

The heap is built by first placing a layer of coarse hedge trimmings, briars or brambles, as the base of the heap, to allow a flow of air under the heap during maturing. This first coarse layer is about a foot thick and ten feet square, and will be repeated for an indefinite length, but it is well to build the heap to its full height of six feet in sections of about ten feet square. Building proceeds in ten-foot square sections, gradually sloping inwards to a width of six feet at a height of six feet.

Upon the layers of hedge trimmings and briars is placed a two- or three-inch layer of softer material such as straw or long grass, to prevent the next layer of manure from falling through. Then a layer of three inches of farmyard manure. This is given a very light dusting of ground limestone and, if possible, though this is not essential, a sprinkling of soil. Both the soil and the ground limestone encourage earthworms and soil bacteria, and though it may not be possible to spread these between each series of layers, every effort is made to place some near the middle and the top of the heap. If sawdust is available, this is put in between each series of layers to a thickness of one inch.

Another foot of dry bulky material such as straw then follows the first series of layers, then three inches of farmyard manure, a sprinkling of ground limestone and soil, sawdust, and repeating the same sequence of layers to the full height of six feet. Sewage sludge is a good activator, as an alternative or supplement to farmyard manure in the heap.

Green but wilted weeds, particularly nettles, dandelion, a few chicory plants complete with roots, cabbage, tomato and potato haulms, charlock, docks, etc., are added with the bulky vegetable layer whenever possible.

The heap is topped off with an inch layer of soil or three to six inches of sawdust. The weathering which this sawdust will receive on top of the heap will be good preparation for its use in the next compost heap (when the present neap is used the sawdust is thrown back, together with any hedge trimmings which may not have rotted and any weeds which may have grown on the heap, for use in the next heap). If these are not available, we use about six inches or more of straw or a few old sacks, to conserve the heat and to prevent too much moisture penetrating the heap in wet districts. This is also beneficial in dry areas to prevent drying out, and in such areas it may also be necessary to add, during the building, enough water to make the heap as moist as a damp sponge.

Incorporation of adequate air is the secret of avoiding turning. The heap is built as lightly as possible and on no account trampled. So long as each layer is in contact with the next layer, no compaction should take place. The main object of turning the heap is to incorporate more air as the heap becomes compact. But if enough air can be admitted by other means, especially in the initial building of the heap, excellent compost can be made without any turning at all.

If time and labour permit, even better compost is made by giving the heap a turn, but with no turn at all, in a period of six months, farm compost to suit the most fastidious farmer is possible.

Where weed seeds or threshing cavings are used in any quantity the heap is turned once to ensure thorough destruction. For this reason we try to confine the threshing cavings and ripe weed seeds to separate heaps, so that we may avoid the need to turn all other heaps.

The cost of making compost by this method is so infinitesimal that it is hardly worth mentioning, except to discount the erroneous though widespread notion that the use of compost is prohibited to the practical farmer because of its cost. Working entirely by hand, except for a tractor and trailer and an ex-army lorry, two of my men can make 500 tons each year at times when they have no other useful work to do, at a cost in labour and materials of £25, or 1s. a ton. If anyone knows a cheaper form of fertilizing the land, let him write to me at once, for I am always interested in further economies.

SELF-SERVICE COMPOST CORNER

We have all seen the 'umbrella' stacks created by cattle which break into a fenced-off haystack in the corner of a field. But it did not occur to me to turn this annoying habit of cattle to advantage until in our second year at Goosegreen the dry cows and heifers, which were outlying, consumed a large quantity of a straw-stack which had been built after threshing, in the field some distance from the farm buildings. I was surprised at the small amount of waste straw which the cattle left, working into the stack from the bottom and pulling it down from above them as they ate their way in. Without the accident of wayward cattle demonstrating this economical system of self-service, I should not have allowed them access to the stack deliberately for fear of large quantities of waste straw being trampled under as it was pulled out. But once more the answer to a nuisance was to make use of it.

So each year since then we have deliberately threshed at least one field of grain in the field and built a stack of straw in the corner. Immediately after harvest the stubble is disced to encourage weed seed germination, and if the grain crop has not been undersown and there is any danger of an inadequate growth of weeds, we sow barn sweepings or threshing screenings to provide something green to grow through the winter. Then our dry cows and young stock winter out either in or with access to this field, taking their daily ration of green food from the weeds, or trefoil and Italian ryegrass if it is there, and supplementing it with as much straw as they care to pull from the stack in the corner of the field. A small amount of the straw is left on the ground, dunged on and trodden in. In the extreme winter the cattle spend their nights around the stack and take their food as they need it. By the early spring the stack is consumed and there remains the manure, which we tidy up into a compost heap to which we add the hedge and ditch trimmings of the same field, and which in the autumn is ready to be spread back on to the same field.

The Soil Association, at their Farm in Haughley, Suffolk, have improved on this system, where a space larger than that occupied by the compost heap can be spared for the rest of the summer. They sow a cereal of some kind, generally rye, over the area covered by the dung and trodden straw around the site of the stack. This is subsequently cut at a convenient time during the year, either green or mature, and incorporated with the manure underneath it in making a compost heap on the spot.

CHAPTER ELEVEN

Field Recording

O ne of the first essentials of sound fertility farming is a detailed knowledge of each field.

To look into a field and contemplate the subsequent operations and cropping, merely on a physical examination of the soil, in many cases not even that, is worse than buying a pedigree dairy cow with no knowledge of its pedigree and milking records of its ancestry.

Before cropping the fields of Goosegreen, when I first came here, my policy was to find out all that I could about the fields; that is, ever since I had my first wheat failure, which a wireworm count *after* the event told me was caused by a million wireworms to the acre.

I've not tackled a field since then without knowing what I was up against.

But more than wireworms, I want to know what each field is capable of in other directions; what treatment must I apply, what crop should I take first, and what sort of rotation may I plan for the field. Is it a field capable of growing the heavy yielding stiff varieties of wheat? Does the field need draining or subsoiling before it is capable of carrying a crop through a wet winter, or if draining or/and subsoiling is needed and not possible, will spring cropping overcome the problem for the time? What are the labour needs of the field; that is, estimated man tractor hours in relation to the likely returns?

It is also interesting to make a worm count and even a bacterial count. The local District Officer of the County Agricultural Committee will make soil analyses free of charge, and it is as well also to persuade him to measure what, in fact, are far more important indications of soil fertility. Though I have included soil analyses among information likely to be of use in determining the cropping of a field, if the organic content of the soil is satisfactory, there are very few crops that will not grow well whatever the soil analysis may be. The only ones that need worry us are the legumes—beans, clover, etc.—which do not readily grow on acid soils. But if there are no worms, and the bacterial count is low, then poor crops of all kinds may be expected, for the sparse populations of earthworms and bacteria mean there is not enough humus to keep them alive, and, as these creatures of the soil suffer nutritionally, so will the crop.

These things are all-important now, but they will be doubly important in the days ahead when farming may only survive as a tolerable occupation by its own efficiency.

By a soil analysis I have saved myself a lot of time and expense on liming which I might otherwise have undertaken. Many farmers have limed field after field on their farms since the increased lime subsidy was announced, simply because it is cheap to do so.

I have seen many fields in my district being given heavy doses of lime, where a physical examination has shown not one symptom of lime deficiency. I am sure it would be a great saving of public money and private time if, where no obvious deficiency exists, a test is taken before applying it. As recently as 1949 I was saved a considerable expenditure on ground limestone in this way. After ten years without lime of any description I decided to apply ground limestone according to requirements on every field. I called in the nearby Castle Hill Quarry analyst and said I intended to lime according to the requirements shown by his analysis. Not a single field indicated any lime requirements. We were both amazed. He said that he had never before sampled the soil of a dairy farm without having got an order for some lime.

I must say I was even more surprised, but it gave me valuable new information besides saving me considerable expense. For it is now evident that organic methods, which include subsoiling and deep-rooting herbs over a period of years, maintain a correct soil balance even on farms which are sending away large quantities of milk. It is the use of chemical manures, particularly sulphate of ammonia, which, far from correcting deficiencies, burn up the natural nutriment of the soil and leave it acid and lacking in various major and trace elements.

Assuming satisfactory drainage, the first crop on newly broken grassland will be winter wheat; but if the field is likely to flood I should winter fallow, disc the field again in spring, and crop to spring wheat or oats.

I must then determine the type of soil in order to decide the variety of wheat. As this varies on most farms, if not in soil type, certainly in fertility, this is very important. It is useless to sow Bersee or Holdfast if the soil is only capable of giving maximum yields from Steadfast or Squarehead Master.

Another aspect of variety choice has been emphasized by the wet weather of some recent summers. That is the necessity of taking every advantage of factors which contribute to an early harvest.

One year I finished harvest on August 17th. It started raining on August 18th and continued nearly every day for weeks, with disastrous results in some parts of the country. The following year I finished corn harvest on August 18th, and while we were bringing in the last few loads it started to rain and persisted without real drying weather for weeks.

It is wise, then, to consider the relative earliness of different fields and to sow the earliest maturing varieties—Bersee, Jubilee Gem, Holdfast, Little Joss—on the fields in which conditions of soil and aspect will make for early ripening.

Further, make careful note of any field which is so fertile that it causes heavy crops of cereals to lodge, so that even if it is not your usual practice to graze them in the spring you will in any case graze hard on those fields inclined to lodge, thus ensuring a short strong straw.

At convenient times it is well to make notes of such additional information about each field as length of time taken to perform the various operations such as discing, cultivating, dragging and later cutting or combining under normal conditions, so that in future years it will be possible to plan out a cropping programme and labour schedule which will take the best from every hour.

I know, for instance, that for discing the field 'Big Broadmead' it will take a half-day and that if my tractor driver starts one morning he will be ready for another job by dinner-time. That if it takes one and a half days to roll the field at the speed which gives the right consolidation I may have something unpleasant to say if my driver asks for another job at the end of a day. Incidentally, in the matter of rolling, the only way to find out the time taken for the proper speed is to do it yourself.

All the information that can be gathered is, of course, recorded. A kind of 'case history' of each field provides an unlimited source of valuable information and guidance for the future, to say nothing of winter evening amusement. From the records book it is then a simple matter to arrive at an accurate costing of each crop in each field.

This record book will be even more valuable as a story of the progress of each field in 'going fertility'; that is, changing over from the disease and infertility producing methods of chemical farming to the fertility

97

farming methods described in this book. You will wish to know how each field starts in its level of fertility or humus content, the stages at which you add compost or green manures and roughly the quantities, and the fields from which you may consequently expect the most healthy crops—and to which you may put any unhealthy animals which are under treatment and therefore need the most fertile grazing.

You will watch the changing colour of each field as it adds each year of fertility farming to its productive capacity, and you will note the increasing speed and economy with which cultivations and cropping operations are carried out. As the years pass you will find that certain operations become unnecessary—for instance, horse hoeing and then hand hoeing will disappear from the record book for each field as it reaches a high state of fertility and as you gain in ability to use its weeds at the right time and control them by surface discing when they are not needed.

Especially valuable will be the knowledge gained by field recording of the milk-producing capacity of each field. It has been a revelation to me to find, by such careful checks, how different fields, though superficially similar in cropping ability, vary widely as producers of milk when grazed as leys by the milking herd. So, in recording leys, in addition to noting the days of grazing each one provides, give a column to the daily milk production from each ley while it is being grazed, noting also for comparison purposes any additional food which may be fed as a supplement to the ley.

No dairy farmer can work efficiently without milk recording. Field recording is, to my mind, just as helpful to the arable and mixed farmer.

CHAPTER TWELVE

Weatherproof Harvesting

A ll sorts of involved mechanical inventions have been introduced to take the worry out of harvesting, from the hay loader and pick-up baler to the combine harvester, none of which can claim to have beaten the weather. All the widely advocated methods of haymaking and harvesting still depend for their success on long spells of dry and sunny weather.

But the simple inventions of a practical Scots agriculturalist, who has spent twenty years perfecting his system, has made haymaking and harvesting a weatherproof operation which any farmer may face with complete equanimity and a minimum of expense.

A Weatherproof Tripod Harvesting System is a natural process of air drying to cure hay and corn in the most catchy of seasons, and because of its simplicity and naturalness is to be preferred to orthodox haymaking or combine harvesting. A sample of seed barley from 100-acre tripodded field was enough to persuade me to give Tripod Harvesting a full-scale trial. This 100-acre crop at Chequers Estate remained in the field throughout the winter of 1946–7, and when threshed in April proved to be unblemished and fit for seed. I have since kept a field of linseed out on tripods all winter, threshed in April, and used it for seed, without loss of a single sheaf.

When haymaking by this system the mowing machine is followed immediately by the kick tedder. This enables the air to be incorporated with the grass and clover immediately to hasten wilting. The old-fashioned kick tedder is most satisfactory for this work, and a Somerset firm is now making the kick tedder once more, after it had been extinct for many years.

On a good drying day what has been tedded in the morning will be fit to put on to the tripods during the afternoon, provided it is not wet with dew or rain. Except with the heaviest of crops, I have usually put on to tripods each day what was cut during the same morning. As there

7a. Cutting and tedding lucerne for tripodding. Note the kick type of tedder which is best for this job.

7b. Tripodded lucerne at Goosegreen.

8a. Building a tripod hut.

8b. Tripodding hay at Goosegreen.

is no rush to make the best use of a spell of good weather, it is wise not to mow more each day than can be tripodded during the following twenty-four hours.

Once they are experienced, I find that two men can build one tripod in approximately twenty minutes (if the grass is long and the men keen, fifteen minutes is enough). I have myself built a normal-sized 'hut' of lucerne in twenty minutes. This means that two men, with the aid of a sweep or rake to bring the hay to the tripod, will build the 'huts' at the rate of at least a ton an hour. Four men building tripod huts, and one man sweeping or raking hay to the builders, will save a crop of approximately two tons to the acre at the rate of an acre an hour.

The hay is laid lightly on the wire which encircles the three legs of the tripod about a foot from the bottom and built up lightly around the air vents astride each leg of the tripod. I will not attempt to describe in detail how it should be done, for any attempt to do it without a practical demonstration will no doubt fail. It is important to see it properly demonstrated by someone who has made tripodded hay successfully. When the 'hut' has reached a height of about eight feet the wooden air-vent constructors are removed, leaving a free passage of air at three points in the base of the 'hut' up through the hollow centre. The building of grain tripods is similar with the sheafs standing upright around the bottom and going up in tiers in as upright a position as possible.

Once on the tripods, both hay and grain are safe from any kind of weather, and the damage from bleaching by the sun and leeching by the rain is avoided. The hay is cured green and remains green permanently, and the corn is matured on the straw as Nature intended, by a steady flow of air through the 'hut.' After two to three weeks, according to the weather, though quite regardless of the *kind* of weather, both hay or grain are ready. Even after a shower of rain a breeze will quickly dry the huts, as they are never more than superficially wet.

The ideal method of dealing with the 'huts' is to sweep the hay to the baler and to sweep the corn to the threshing machine by means of Proctor's sweep which carries the hut intact with tripod legs inside. One sweep driven by tractor or Jeep can keep a full-size baler or threshing machine going.

We discovered very soon that there is an art in tripodding, which makes expert instruction essential to success; for, like many others, we spoiled some of the crop by working, in the beginning, without

PREPARING FOR THE CHANGE

BUILDINGS (*See plan on page 236*).

The first thing to receive attention in any change of plans, or reconstruction of a farm for the change over to new methods, are the farm buildings. So I give a plan of the ideal layout for the methods I describe. This layout is based on the present layout of my own farm; only *based*, I regret, though I hope one day to achieve the ideal which I consider this plan provides.

Farmers who are fortunate enough to be starting from scratch in the provision of farm buildings, or those who have enough capital to alter existing buildings to an ideal plan, will find this layout most economical of time, labour and materials, for the practice of the methods of farming set out in this book.

The cost of erecting such a set of farm buildings from scratch would be high in 1950. But five percent on the cost, assuming you can raise it, would be small expenditure for an easily workable set of farm buildings; for you can be sure that it will be more than saved every year in reduced labour costs.

When I adapted my farm to a layout as nearly approaching my ideal, though most of the buildings are still more tumbledown than orderly, I saved the wages of two men in the first year. In two years I had paid for the milking parlour and minor alterations to other buildings out of the reduced labour bill.

EQUIPMENT

I have found the following to be the necessary equipment for a farm the size of mine, that is 180 acres approximately. This may be taken to cover the needs of farms from 100 to 200 acres, and the initial requirements of farms of greater acreage. For farms of 200 to 350 acres, start with this equipment and extras will make themselves necessary as work proceeds.

A Tractor. I have some steep hills, and must therefore have a fairly high-powered tractor. For eight years I have done all my work with a 27 h.p. model. An additional light tractor on such heavy and steep land, though far from being an essential, would enable one to effect some economy on much of the lighter work. Or, on level ground, it would be possible to do all the work with the modern hydraulic integral equipment tractor of 16–22 h.p.

A Two-furrow Plough. On light land of good humus content I am convinced that a plough is not necessary. But on all other soils, especially where the humus content is low, it will be necessary to build up the humus content of the topsoil, and thus its friability and ease of work-ing, before it will be possible to dispense entirely with the plough.

Reaper, Binder. Both obvious needs.

Disc Harrow. This is the key implement of the organic farm and one which is capable of performing all the operations of cultivation and seed-bed preparation. Where economy is necessary, no other cultivat-ing implement need be owned. Even a roller may be dispensed with, for a weighted disc harrow, run with the discs straight out, will serve admirably in the compression of a seed-bed.

A Roller is, however, not an expensive implement to buy. They are often available at farm sales at ridiculously low prices, and will be useful in the early stages of working towards completely organic methods. When the soil is rich in organic matter there will be no need for the roller.

Tractor Trailer. A low-loading trailer is preferable, for the nearer to the ground the bed of the trailer the easier is loading and unloading. For though some unloading is to barns and stacks at a height, the greater part of the year the trailer will be engaged in carrying materials which are to be loaded from the ground level and unloaded to the same level.

Light Drag Harrows, for covering seed and grass harrowing.

Two Hundred to Three Hundred Tripods are really an essential in the British climate for the farm desiring self-sufficiency in foodstuffs.

A Hay Tedder. The old-fashioned kick tedder, though not absolutely essential, is a valuable tool for getting air into the grass immediately after cutting, for the purpose of tripodding, and also where quick-wilt-ing is called for in silage making (during excessively wet weather).

A Milking Machine, if you are to milk more than twenty cows.

Some kind of *green-crop loader*, though not essential in the early stages, will be found well worth its cost where much silage is to be made with a small staff. A second trailer, or old army lorry, is also valu-able unless you can borrow one at harvest and muck-carting times.

Starting with these implements, plus all the small tackle like forks, shovels and tools, we can push ahead with the actual farming. I have avoided anything superfluous in the equipping of the farm, and like-wise, throughout the farming notes for the year, I have cut out all the fancy work.

In starting this system of farming you will wonder what the hard cash savings are likely to be, even in the first year, and also how soon some benefit might be expected to result. Though these things will become apparent to some extent as we work through the year, it might be some encouragement to anticipate one or two items.

9a. Bulls are tethered out most of the year, and taken for a walk daily.

9b. A prize-winning home-bred yearling bull Polden Polo by Polden Popomack out of Polden Lou-Lou—tethered in Lucerne and Timothy.

10b. 'Osiris' branching-headed wheat grown experimentally for the first time in Britain by the author.

10a. Seven-inch wheat heads grown on land unploughed and without artificial manures for many years.

Firstly, you will see that we have saved quite £500 on equipment, for the average farm of this size needs at least an additional tractor and supporting equipment under orthodox methods. We may further count on a saving of at least another £500 in labour and another £5 an acre for annual crops—i.e. cereals and roots—in the cost of operations which are avoided by fertility farming methods. In other words, the cash saving in equipment is at least £3 an acre and in labour and cost of operations £5 to £8 an acre. The first saving is not a recurring one. But the £5 to £8 saved in labour and cultivation is both a recurring and an increasing economy, and may represent the profits in the early years (see Chapter Two for details). So, whereas you might have expected some slight fall in returns due to the abandoning of artificial fertilizer and other exploitive practices, the saving effected by the considerable labour and power economies will well balance that and may even make enough difference to turn a loss by orthodox methods into an immediate useful profit by fertility farming methods.

It is useless tackling these methods with the idea that immediate and spectacular results will be obtained. It takes two or three years to begin to see the effects of these methods, particularly where a generation of extractive chemical methods have to be overcome. Where disease has become prevalent in crops or stock, then, however, the first year *will* see remarkable improvement, and enough to convince an intelligent farmer of the ultimate immense benefits which fertility farming will bring. The mere omission of chemical manures and veterinary injections, the stopping of drugs to the soil and the animals, will show an immediate, almost startling, improvement in the health of the animals. Once your mind is set on these natural reforms in soil and livestock management, you may safely say good-bye to the diseases which are so common in herds still under the grip of orthodox 'science.' This does not mean diseases will be eliminated in the first year. It does mean, however, that you will see undeniable signs of their reduction and the clear beginnings of their control and eventual elimination. It will take two generations of home-bred stock to work out hereditary weaknesses, and even then there will be occasional troubles which are inexplicable. But disease, as it is known on most farms to-day, will be no more on the fertility farm after three to five years of rigorous adherence to the methods of this book. The results in the changing character of the soil and the increased yields of crops are not so immediately apparent. For it has taken centuries to remove the humus from the soil, and it will take a few years to get it back to a vital friable condition again. Even so, it is unbelievable how much more quickly it is possible to build fertility than to destroy it. In this fact lies the only hope for the survival of humanity. For were it possible to destroy fertility as quickly as it is to rebuild it, man would have starved himself from the face of the earth half a century ago.

Signs of fertility in the soil which may be watched for as indicators of success are the appearance, in large quantities, of weeds like chickweed. Chickweed will not grow in abundance on poor soil. At Goosegreen it grows, even through the winter, sufficiently to provide large quantities of winter grazing and green manuring. When we started there wasn't a plant of chick-weed anywhere. The earthworm is the best indicator of an increasing humus content. Look for vigorous red worms whenever the soil is moved. The more there are, the more satisfied you may feel about the cropping capacity of the field. At least one in every handful of soil is what you may expect when fertility is at a high level and what you may hope to achieve when you have put every field through a complete cropping rotation by fertility farming methods.

A comfortable carpet-like effect underfoot will also come to the fields after three or four years of humus building, and heavy soil, unpleasant to walk across in wet weather because of clinging mud, will acquire increasingly the clean and spongy condition which allows treading without carrying mud which collects like snowballs on your boots. But this is something to look for in future years and a sign that your farm is truly fertile and healthy.

UNIT ROTATION

Assuming the rotation recommended in the earlier part of this book is to be followed, it is a good plan to divide the farm into units of twelve acres for each 100 of the farm, using one unit for each 100 acres of the farm for each year of the rotation. This means that for each 100 acres the cropping will be as follows:

1st year   12 acres divided into 4 acres kale; 4 acres arable silage crop; 4 acres beans or linseed, getting a 10–12 tons an acre dressing of compost.
2nd year   12 acres oats, or dredge corn under or after sown.
3rd year   12 acres ley—grazed.
4th year   12 acres ley—mown and grazed.
5th year   12 acres ley—grazed and mown; compost 5 tons an acre in winter.
6th year   12 acres ley—grazed and ploughed for autumn cropping.
7th year   12 acres wheat, undersown with legume.
8th year   12 acres—8 acres oats—4 acres barley (if pigs kept).

That is a total of ninety-six acres of rotation crops, leaving four acres per 100 for lucerne or semi-permanent silage crop of some kind.

For every 100 acres of the farm you will then have:

> 20 acres oats, or dredge corn,
> 12 acres wheat (or other cereal),
> 4 acres kale,
> 4 acres beans and/or linseed,
> 4 acres silage crop in addition to ley and lucerne silage,
> 4 acres barley (or additional oats if no pigs),
> 48 acres ley,
> 4 acres lucerne,

which will provide the food for 20 cows and 12 followers in the second year, and 30 cows and 20 followers, plus 5 breeding sows and 500 hens (taking advantage of some purchased foods for pigs and poultry), when the full rotation is working and all the farm is under the four-year ley cropping.

So, with these beginnings we may work through a typical fertility farming year—commencing with the first week in September.

CHAPTER FOURTEEN

Fifty-two Weeks' Farming

SEPTEMBER: 1st Week

The first job of the autumn is to order seeds. Indeed, this ought to be done just as soon as the cropping is decided upon.

Order at the following rates:

Wheat:	3 bushels (180 lb.) an acre.
Oats:	$1\frac{1}{2}$ cwts. (1 sack) an acre.
Beans:	2 cwts. (1 sack) an acre.
Oats and Vetches:	2 bushels / 1 bushels } an acre. (for silage mixture)
Barley:	3 bushels an acre.

Reduce by 25 percent, if to be sown by mid-September, in good seed-bed of high humus content.

Get the disc harrows into the stubbles just as soon as possible—and whenever the opportunity occurs.

You will probably tackle one or two fields first, and it is probably wise to concentrate on a proportion of the farm in the first year.

Choose a field in good heart, with a topsoil containing ample organic matter as indicated by its crumbly friability. A corn stubble, or the ground from which the potatoes have been harvested, is a good place to start. If possible, choose a field that has had no chemical manures in recent years: for this will contain more of the soil organisms, earthworms and fungi that are an essential part of nature's own cultivation and nutriment of the crop. The more earthworms and fungi (the white threads which surround a healthy root development) the more successful will undisturbed soil be.

If there is not ample evidence of organic matter in the soil, either apply a dressing of compost or well-rotted farmyard manure, or sow a green-manuring crop such as rye, mustard or lupins. In either case, the first operation after clearance of the previous crop should be twice working with the disc harrows. If the surface is too hard and dry for the discs to make much impression, the field is probably not fit for a trial of ploughless cropping. But once or twice over the field with the fixed-tine cultivator will bring up sufficient soil to make the disc harrow workable. The only danger in using the cultivator on soil lacking organic matter is that it will bring up clods that quickly bake and harden in the wind and sun, and must then await rain before the field can be prepared for drilling. To avoid this risk, no more should be cultivated each day than can also be worked immediately after with the disc harrow. In later years, when the soil is rich in humus, the cultivator will never be necessary, and the disc harrow will do all that is needed to prepare a first-class seed-bed.

If a green-manuring crop is sown, allow it to grow as near to the stage of flowering as time will allow before sowing the main crop, for the nearer to maturity the green-manuring crop is the more valuable will be its content. Then work it into the surface soil with the disc harrow. If the discs are sharp enough and the harrow is well weighted the green crop can be cut up so finely that the corn drill will run freely at sowing time. I have chopped up on the surface in this way a stemmy crop of kale five feet in height effectively enough to follow with the disc drill, sowing oats.

Sow the seed at the normal rate of seeding on soil of average fertility, or, if the soil is rich in humus, up to 25 percent less may be sown. A thin seeding on soil which offers the ideal medium for germination, tillering and growth, will produce a much heavier yield than a heavy seeding on the same soil. The sowing of individual seeds in soil which offers a guarantee of a 90 percent or more germination, as soil managed naturally would, is of course the ideal which will be practised when a suitable drill is available. For in undisturbed humus-rich surface soil nothing is likely to go wrong and the usual margin of heavy seeding rate is not necessary. My unploughed wheat crops often look so thin during the winter that I feel sure they will have to be patched, yet they are often too thick by harvest time.

At least one piece of early wheat should be sown for grazing in the early spring, or even late autumn if growth is good. The oats and vetches for silage-making next May should be sown as early as possible after the end of August.

Where any lime deficiency exists, now is a good time to apply ground limestone, to be worked into the surface soil during cultivations before autumn croppings. It is not necessary to have a soil analysis in order to decide whether lime is needed. And the fact that your land may overlie chalk does not mean to say it will not benefit from an application of ground limestone. It may be that the calcium in your soil is in a non-available condition. It may be that you have a chalk subsoil which is locked away from the topsoil by a hard ploughpan. It is wise then to try a strip of land with a dressing of ground limestone and note for yourself the effect.

Indicators of a need for lime are the soft mat-like tread of an old pasture and the appearance of any of the following plants in profusion: red sorrel, silver weed, yarrow, ragwort; and a general tendency to excessive weediness.

If a subsoiler can be hired and used on the fields to be limed, lasting benefit will be derived from the work. But subsoiling will be unnecessary once deep-rooting herbs have been included in a ley on each field.

Rates of application will vary according to the type of soil, but an application of three tons to the acre of ground limestone or natural chalk can usually be reckoned to be beneficial.

Lime the fields that are to carry one of the following crops if you must limit your liming to a part of the farm: clover ley, barley and sugar beet, oats and vetch mixture, and lucerne. Crops that will tolerate acidity are wheat, oats when sown alone, linseed and potatoes. Fields that are to carry these crops may be limed in a later year.

SEPTEMBER: 3rd Week

GREEN MANURING

Catch crops sown now or as soon as possible after harvest will store soil nitrogen for the coming spring. Fields that do not need to be cropped at once should be sown with mustard for green manuring. Sow at the rate of 20 lb. an acre, broadcast, after discing the surface. A month to six weeks of growth will give tons of green manure; if the mustard can be allowed, by earlier sowing or longer growing, to become stemmy and approach or reach the flowering stage, the amount of bulky organic matter available to disc into the topsoil will be greater.

Lift potatoes and clamp them under straw. Cover with earth before winter frosts come.

Take the last cut or grazing of lucerne in time to allow the leaves of the plant to grow again before the winter; it may be grazed again in late winter or early spring to discourage predominance of grasses.

If there is a flush of grass and clover on the leys that is not likely to be cleared up before the winter comes, cut it for silage. On the lighter dry soils it may be left for winter grazing. The needs of the animals will be greater in the winter.

Autumn-calving heifers and cows will be approaching due dates, and should be watched more closely and given rather more feeding than usual. They should calve down in healthy blooming condition, but not uncomfortably fat. Forcing with concentrated foods before calving—a system known as 'steaming up'—is not to be recommended. Give the animal ample natural food, but avoid high-protein foods which put too much strain on the heifer's system at the most critical stage of her life and result in milk fever in cows—due to the double stimulus of high-protein diet and parturition. A heifer on good grass should be in quite good enough condition to calve down and do well. There is no need to bring her in to calve unless it is for convenience. The field is the natural, and therefore the ideal, calving place.

Watch the milk yields and be prepared to supplement the grass which is now losing its nutritional value. If you have ample kale, a small load of kale—about 10 lb. per head per day—will keep them going for the time being. It will also be necessary to start feeding a production

117

ration—3 lb. oats and1 lb. linseed and/or bean meal for each gallon of milk over one gallon—to the heavier yielding cows.

SEPTEMBER: 4th Week

Every stubble on the farm should be worked with disc harrows thoroughly, to germinate weed seeds. You are really preparing a seed-bed for the most valuable fertility crop—weeds—which will hold the remaining nitrogen of the season and contribute food for winter grazing and humus for next spring's crops.

Where a field is to receive an autumn dressing of compost, and this is especially necessary in the field which is to be sown to beans, apply it now so that it may be worked into the surface. Put out the compost in heaps and leave in heaps until it can be spread and worked immediately into the topsoil. This will be compost that was made six months ago, unless you are only just starting—though you may still have a little of that prepared last autumn if it was not all used on the kale field.

Ten to twelve tons an acre of compost will be sufficient if the soil is in reasonably good heart. A rough estimate of weight may be made by calculating 15 cwt. per cubic yard of mature compost (see Appendix for estimating weights). This application is given once in the rotation, with the addition of 5 tons an acre on the ley before it is broken—if supplies allow. In conjunction with green manuring and undersowing of cereal crops at every opportunity, this will build and maintain a high level of fertility.

The area for the oats and vetches for next year's arable silage crop should now be sown, having applied compost first, if possible; though in emergency compost *may* be spread next May after the crop is cut. Any variety of oats will do for this purpose, though in areas of severe frosts what is needed to enable silage-making to start early is a frost-resistant variety such as Grey Winter oats. On poor land rye should be used instead of oats. Winter vetches should be mixed with the oats or rye at the rate of $1\frac{1}{2}$ bushels of vetches to $1\frac{1}{2}$ bushels of oats or rye. Tick or horse beans may be added at the rate of $\frac{1}{2}$ bushel an acre, though while giving increased bulk and nutritional value does tend to make the mixture expensive in proportion to the resultant yield of green food.

Vetches are now expensive and, if economy is necessary, 1 cwt. oats to $\frac{1}{2}$ cwt. vetches gives a good yield of green crop.

Men not engaged on autumn cultivations and cropping should start now to trim all the hedges and clean the banks and ditches of the farm. All material except the thick branches of trees should be collected for use in the compost heap. *Under no circumstances* should any hedge, ditch or bank material be burnt, no matter how weedy it is. The heat of the compost heap will kill all weed seeds and the resultant compost derived from a wide variety of herbs, grasses and hedgerow bushes, together with a small proportion of animal waste, will contain all the essential elements of plant nutrition.

Milk recording sheets and registers should be prepared for the year-end. Animals likely to be not worth recording in the new recording year should be disposed of, or removed from the herd until they can be, so that they need not be entered in the register and paid for.

OCTOBER: 1st Week

You will need now to think about threshing. Book the contractor in time to get out some of your own grain for seed. Grain that has been in stack for less than six weeks will be in the middle of the 'sweat' which always follows stacking, so if threshed then should be used immediately.

Beans should be sown early October, if at all possible; and when one early piece of wheat for spring grazing, and the oats and vetches for silage, have been sown, the beans should come next before sowing any other grain crop.

Beans should be sown at the rate of 2 cwt. an acre. There are no named varieties of field bean. While you are sowing the field bean you may like also to sow a corner of the field to broad beans for the house or even for sale. Early broad beans are a profitable crop, and sown now they would catch the early market.

OCTOBER: 2nd Week

Young stock out on low-lying fields should be watched for possible husk. If you notice any of them giving a throaty cough bring them in at once, or transfer them to a high ley where the husk worm is usually not prevalent. See *Cure Your Own Cattle* for treatment.

Begin to plan available food supplies. Production ration requirements may be worked out by estimating the likely milk yields of the cows and reckoning that for each gallon of milk you will need approximately 3 lb. oats and 1 lb. linseed or beans. A cow that is likely to give 500 gallons of milk during the winter months should therefore be allowed approximately a ton of meal. This will be the maximum requirement of all except the exceptional milkers, and if you have 15 cwt. of oats and 5 cwt. of linseed or beans for each cow you can reckon yourself very well supplied, and with a sufficient margin to feed the young stock a small ration daily up to the age of nine months.

For maintenance you should also have 1 ton of hay for each cow and 5 cwt. for each head of young stock—unless you are relying mainly on silage for the cows instead of hay, when you will need double the quantity in silage. Oat and wheat straw should be available *ad lib*.

Winter Feeding

The following will give some guidance in planning for self-sufficiency in winter feeding stuffs. It cannot of course be an accurate estimate for every farm. It is what has proved effective under my own conditions. But it will serve as a useful guide to be adapted with experience to varying standards of soil fertility.

Estimate for a period of approximately 170 days which, for calculating purposes, 1 lb. a day a head will equal approximately $1\frac{1}{2}$ cwt. for the winter period.

Kale. Allow an average of 30 lb. daily for cows: 45 cwt.; 10 lb. daily for young stock: 15 cwt. On an estimated yield of 15 tons an acre this means that a herd of equal numbers of cows and young stock would need one-fifth acre a cow.

Silage. Allow the same quantities as kale, that is 3 tons each cow, to provide for cattle of all ages when young stock and cows are equal numbers.

On an arable silage crop of, say, oats and vetches this can be grown on one-third acre, so that a herd of 30 cows and 30 followers would need 10 acres of oats and vetches or similar silage crop.

Hay. If hay is to form the bulk of your maintenance ration, allow 15 lb. a cow and 8 lb. a head young stock, or just over 1 ton per cow and 12 cwt. each for young stock.

If the allowance of kale and silage are as above, and you have oat straw for bulky dry fodder, then hay may be dispensed with altogether except for the youngest stock only, when an average allowance of 5 to 8 lb. a head, with some kale or silage, will be enough for cattle up to eighteen months old.

PRODUCTION RATIONS

Cereals. Allow 3 lb. per gallon of milk or 1 ton (approximately) for a 700-gallon cow, which on average yields is 1 acre of oats per cow.

Protein Food. 1 lb. per gallon of milk, which for 700 gallons may be obtained from $\frac{1}{2}$ acre per cow of linseed and/or beans.

As grass will supply the production requirements of a large part of the milk yield, the above production allowances will cover the requirements of young stock.

GRAZING REQUIREMENTS

On first-class leys, including the deep-rooting herbs on strong fertile land, 1 acre should feed one cow and one head of young stock throughout the summer.

On poorer land and less-productive leys allow $1\frac{1}{4}$ acres per cow and $\frac{3}{4}$ acre per head of young stock. An additional acre per head of young stock and dry cows will be needed for winter grazing, supplemented by oat straw and/or kale or silage, and winter weed grazing.

To summarize, the requirements of a dairy herd on a per cow basis, assuming equal numbers of young stock, are:

Kale	$\frac{1}{5}$ acre per cow
Arable silage crop	$\frac{1}{3}$ acre per cow
Hay (permanent grass)	1 acre per cow
Hay (seeds ley)	$\frac{1}{2}$ acre per cow
Oats	1 acre per cow
Linseed and/or beans	$\frac{1}{2}$ acre per cow
Grazing (good)	1 acre per cow
Grazing (poor)	2 acres per cow
Winter grazing	1 acre per cow

OCTOBER: 3rd Week

You should have cut out mangolds if you planned for enough silage, but in case you grew some as a first-year insurance, then both mangolds and sugar beet should now be lifted. While you are lifting the mangolds, consider again all the labour involved in growing this crop and decide that silage and kale will completely replace your mangolds next year. On the fertility farm there is really no need to go to the expense of growing mangolds.

Sugar beet is a different proposition, especially on the poor-landfarm. There is no better crop for helping to restore fertility. Sugar beet is a deep-rooting plant which needs to be well composted and limed. This means that if the sugar beet pays no profits at all it does leave behind a field in very good heart for the following cereal crop; and if the tops are left on the field, and the pulp is returned from the factory, all that goes off the field is the sugar and some moisture.

While it is possible to clamp mangolds complete with their tops, it is better for soil fertility that the tops should be left on the field. The extra labour involved is well repaid in subsequent crops.

Wheat and oat sowing should continue with all possible speed now. So long as the seed-bed has sufficient coverage of soil for the crop, it does not matter if the surface is rough. The winter frosts will soon level the field and break up any clods that may remain.

Sow wheat and oats of the following varieties on the soil indicated:

Soil of	Wheat	Rate of Seeding lb.	Oats	Rate of Seeding cwt.
High Fertility	Holdfast	180	S. 172	$1\frac{1}{2}$
	Pilot	,,	S. 147	,,
	Yeoman	,,	Picton	,,
	Bersee	,,		
Medium Fertility	Pilot	,,	Grey Winter	,,
	Bersee, Warden	,,	Marvellous	,,
	Squarehead II	,,	Resistance	,,
	Squareheads Master	,,		
Low Fertility	Little Joss	200	Grey Winter	2
	Squareheads Master	,,	Bountiful	,,

OCTOBER: 4th Week

Autumn-calving cows should be carefully watched when approaching calving. The best place for them to calve is still in the field, providing the nights are not excessively wet. You may prefer, however, to bring them into a box for your own comfort in visiting them at nights. Don't interfere with a cow that is calving unless she appears to be having a protracted calving. Most cows like to get on without fuss or attention and are generally capable of managing without assistance.

The cow should be on a light diet for a few days before calving, of mainly green food. The dung should be loose, otherwise the green food should be increased. If there is any tendency to constipation, give linseed oil or molasses—1 to 2 pints daily.

Allow the cow to eat her placenta after calving if she wishes. It contains hormones which are needful for the flow of milk. But keep an eye on her in case she has difficulty in swallowing it.

After the cow has finished licking the calf and settled down, a drink of warm water is all she needs for a few hours. After about twelve hours a bran mash would be helpful, i.e. a bucketful of bran damped with hot water.

Let the cow have her calf for a few days. The suckling by the calf will stimulate milk secretion and encourage the flow of the hormones that ensure udder health. If you can continue to let the calf have one of the cow's quarters while you milk the rest, allowing a different quarter for the calf each time, both cow and calf will be under conditions as ideal as practical economics allow. Failing that, put the calf on to a foster mother, giving half a gallon of milk daily for Channel Island or Kerry cattle, or 8 to 10 lb. for other breeds.

If the udder is at all inflamed or hard, keep the cow on a laxative diet of bran mashes and green food only. Hot and cold alternate fomentations of the hard part of the udder are a good thing. If the milk is ropy or clotted, fast the cow completely and follow instructions for treatment of Mastitis, Chapter 20.

Go on with hedge trimming and ditch cleaning, collecting the material for compost. Allow nothing to be burned.

123

NOVEMBER: 1st Week

Compost making should be in full swing now.

The rush of autumn sowing will have eased a little unless there have been weather hold-ups, and compost for use in the spring should now be made in fields for kale, so as to allow six months for maturing. See that ample air is incorporated so that turning may be avoided. The object of turning is to incorporate more air; if the heap is built sufficiently loose to maintain a good admixture of air, turning can be avoided. That is not to say that turning does not produce better compost. But garden compost it is always worth while to turn at least once. For the farm, where a coarser-textured finished product is satisfactory, the aim should be to avoid turning.

If the harvest has been difficult there will be a heavy seeding of self-sown crops. This provides an occasion when it will be good policy to change from the set rotation in order to take the fullest advantage of these self-sown seeds. Where beans were harvested try to fit in a crop that will take advantage of them. An oat and vetch mixture, or a dredge corn mixture, are two crops that will utilize to the full the self-sown beans. It is safe to sow the same cereal again after a first straw crop that has a heavy self-sown crop, but where a second straw crop is taken make a note to undersow with a trefoil/Italian ryegrass mixture for green manuring after harvest. Linseed is another crop that sheds heavily in a late harvest and it is a good crop to follow with a green silage mixture, for the young green linseed, which will be cut with the silage crop if it survives winter frosts, is especially valuable medicinally. Self-sown crops are always far in advance of the later sown chosen crop because of the natural method of sowing and longer time in the ground. Above all, the utilization of self-sown crops is valuable psychologically to the state of mind of the farmer, for it is satisfying compensation for a bad harvest.

Spread straw around any muddy gateways or where cows tend to gather—this will help to make manure and at the same time keep cows and gateways clean.

NOVEMBER: 2nd Week

Autumn rains will give you a chance to see that all drains and ditches are running. If water stands in any part of the farm it should be let off now and a note should be taken to subsoil the patches that are not free draining. Subsoiling is within the reach of even the smallest farmer now that hydraulic lift subsoiling attachments are available at about £25.

Thereafter take an opportunity during the winter to subsoil the grassland, and when a dry enough spell comes, arable land that is not cropped may also be subsoiled.

Most of the milking cows should now be on a production ration of home-grown oats and linseed or beans. See Appendix for supplies if home-grown crops are inadequate. Cattle giving more than a gallon a day should have 4 lb. per gallon each day of a suitable production ration. Cows giving a gallon or less should get along very well on grass and a small green kale or root supplement.

Take the bull a walk every day. He should still be tethered out to grass, utilizing all the waste corners about the farm that would otherwise be unproductive. The busy part of the year is approaching for the bull and, particularly if he is getting on in years, he must be given all the exercise possible, otherwise he will quickly become a slow worker.

NOVEMBER: 3rd Week

Heifers for next autumn calving may now be put with the bull.

In the North of England and Scotland milking cows will need to be indoors at nights, but in the south whether or not they are brought in will depend on a number of circumstances. They are healthier out all the year round, but they will need rather more food to keep themselves warm during the frosty nights. If a large amount of manure is to be made, and there is ample straw for bedding, it is a good plan to bring them into an open yard, or fenced-off corner of a paddock just for the night. A plan which I have operated successfully is to bed down a corner of a grass field with plenty of wheat straw. This encourages them to use that corner for nights, with the result that there is by the spring a collection of manure-soaked straw with which to make compost in the corner of that field—with the addition of hedge trimmings, etc., from the same field.

Another factor is the condition of the soil. A heavy, wet soil is not suitable for cows to winter out on. The pounding of the cows' feet on such land would soon ruin the grass in wet weather.

It will be necessary to start feeding kale and hay on a winter scale around this time. Full winter rations should not be given at once. A few forkfuls of hay may be scattered on the grass, or, what is more convenient, a small cartload of kale. The hay is better kept back until the cows are indoors.

Alternatively run an electric fence across the kale field in a zigzag line. Without detaching the wire, alternate stakes may be moved forward each day.

NOVEMBER: 4th Week

Late sowing of wheat and oats should be done as soon as possible. The weather will limit the number of days that may be spent sowing corn this month, but so long as the soil is dry enough to enable the drags or discs to cover the seed after sowing, it does not matter how rough or moist the soil is. There is an old saying about wheat sowing: 'In heavy, out heavy,' which means that wheat sown under heavy conditions usually yields heavily.

Most winter varieties of wheat and oats may be sown up to early December, though the yield will diminish as December is approached in the date of sowing. After the beginning of December it is better to wait until the end of January and sow Atle or Bersee wheat, S.147 or S.172 oats (on strongest land only), or a true spring oat.

If the weather is too bad, or the field too damp to sow with a drill in the ordinary way, it may be possible to broadcast the seed and go over it afterwards with a light harrow. Never sow seed at this time of year unless you can cover it immediately, for the later the season the more thorough are the ravages of rooks and other birds in search of winter food.

One way of sowing a crop, which my Italian cowman has experienced in Italy, is to broadcast the seed and turn a flock of sheep into the field to cover it by trampling it in. This might be tried if it gets too wet to cover the seed by normal means. But with fertility farming methods—keeping organic matter on top and dispensing with the plough—you will soon cease to be dependent on the weather.

NOVEMBER: 5th Week

If it gets too wet to disc land for spring cropping, and some ploughing is still being done, fields which are not carrying a winter grazing crop may be ploughed during November and December. This enables the winter frosts to work on the furrows which are left rough so that an easily workable seed-bed is produced by the time of sowing in the spring.

DECEMBER: 1st Week

CATTLE FEEDING IN DECEMBER

On reasonably dry farms, or on land that may be poached without danger to subsequent crops, cattle may be folded on kale or turnips. For this purpose I like to have a piece of kale that is not too well grown. The leafy thousand-headed kale, or hungry gap kale, or rape kale, should have been sown during last summer, to provide the best type of winter grazing; though even with a thick-stemmed crop of marrow-stem kale I should not hesitate to graze if labour for cutting is scarce. It merely means that some of the coarser stems will be left behind after the cattle, but I have successfully tackled a field covered with long, thick, upright stems of kale and prepared it for spring oats without any trouble. The heavy disc harrow will usually cut the stems into tiny pieces which offer no hindrance to the corn drill, provided the field is crossed a sufficient number of times with the disc harrow.

If root grazing is out of the question, then it is to be hoped that you have laid in a good store of silage and oat straw. These are my standby for the winter, though, if there is good hay as well, all the better.

Everything else—and even the calves have a goodly ration of it-thrive healthily on silage, kale and oat straw which was cut while it still had some green in the straw. If fed with the oat still in the ear, this is equal to good hay; and if saved on tripods it is even better than most hay.

DECEMBER: 2nd Week

HEDGING

Though easier to do while sap is still in the stems, hedging is a job that gets left till the winter more often than not.

Hedges that have become overgrown and gappy should be laid. If the hedge is too wide the sides should be trimmed down, separately heaping along the headlands of the field all the soft material of the hedge and any stems which do not exceed the thickness of your little finger. This soft material should later be carried to the site of the compost heap, together with the cleaning from the ditches. The coarse material should be stacked in heaps for firewood, or if unsuitable for that they may be burned near the compost heaps to provide wood ash for incorporation in the heap during building.

When the sides are trimmed back to the middle of the hedge, main branches and trunks should be cut out, leaving sufficient long coarse wood to be cut only deeply enough to enable the upright branches and trunks to be bent over and intertwined with stakes inserted in the hedge or the lower half of trunks that have been allowed to remain in the hedge. The important point to watch in the layering of hedges is that the cut diagonally across the trunk of the sapling or small tree that is to be plaited into the hedge should be on the side away from the sun, so that the trunk may be laid towards the sun. This will ensure a strong growth in the right direction. If the hedge is laid away from the sun the tendency will be for the hedge to grow backwards towards the sun, eventually resulting in an untidy hedge which will be more difficult to trim in future years.

The main purpose of hedging is to keep hedges within reasonable bounds. Do not cut trees, and allow growth vertically, once the gaps are filled. Both shelter and leaf fall are essential to the farm, and the water-holding capacity of good hedges is important.

With plenty of organic matter in the topsoil and deep-rooting herbs in the leys—except on sea-level land—drainage problems will be dealt with naturally; and the former need to tile-drain and keep ditches running is no longer important. But this ideal state is not reached for a few years, and in the meantime it is well to watch the flow of tile drains.

DECEMBER: 3rd Week

Silage, the best of all winter foods, may be fed for production at the rate of 15 to 20 lb. per gallon of milk produced, according to the quality of silage. As little as 10 lb. to the gallon of the very best silage has been known with a Jersey. Don't worry about feeding too much if you have ample. Orthodox experts advise us not to feed more than about 50 to 60 lb.; but, unless the animal's palate is being perverted by a diet too rich in concentrated protein and other stimulants, her own stomach will tell her when she has had enough of such natural food as silage—particularly if the silage is made without the addition of preservatives, acids or such like, or if it has received only crude molasses, which is itself an unrefined natural product.

If you have made the mistake of using acids in the preparation of silage, then of course you must limit very carefully the quantity of silage you feed.

December provides an opportunity to tidy the farm. The yard mud should be scraped up and taken to the site of the compost heap to provide the small proportion of soil needed for the making of good compost.

DECEMBER: 4th Week

Spread any dung droppings on pastures which have had no attention or on fields from which cows have recently been moved. Use the harrows as opportunity presents itself. Remember, on the dairy farm, that the grass is the most important crop, which means that any work which is improving the ley or old grass field is at all times the most important job on the farm, no matter what other work there is to be done.

Fence gaps before they get worse.

SOIL FOR COMPOST

Collecting soil for the compost heaps is a tedious and generally neglected job on the busy mixed farms. Every opportunity should therefore be taken during the winter to scrape up the yards and thus accumulate a heap of dung-impregnated soil for use in the spring compost making. This also gives a good purpose to an otherwise not very popular job. Few farm men like scraping muddy yards merely for the sake of a tidy appearance, but if they are persuaded of the value of this ingredient to the compost heap they may even become enthusiastic about keeping the yard clean and tidy.

JANUARY: 1st Week

Though we commence the farming year in September, we cannot escape forward thoughts at the time of New Year and some planning for the future. January is the time of good resolutions, so we may devote the first weeks of the year to listing the things which are essential to the welfare of the farm, soil, crops and livestock.

The modern tendency to encourage factory methods on the farm is removing the traditional peasant's feeling for the soil and livestock, and has brought in recent years an enormous increase in what has been called 'soil banditry.' Sir Albert Howard says that science has taught us not to be better farmers but to be more efficient soil bandits. Good farming is a process of building up, not one of exploitation, though modern business methods and factory farming encourage the latter.

But nature gives nothing without payment in her own currency. It is useless to pay in man-made currency, for nature cannot use it.

Gather together during this month all organic wastes that can be found around the farm. Get hold of all the straw you can—from neighbours, if they can spare it. Many waste it or burn it and may prefer to let you have it. Fetch sawdust and sewage sludge from the town while there is no field work for tractor or lorry.

If you have a grass field or ley which you wish to encourage for early bite, give it a light dressing of straw, or, better still, if you can spare it, a little compost—to keep the soil warm and keep bacterial activity going during frosty weather.

JANUARY: 2nd Week

If your cows are yarded at this time, get them out for exercise for as long a period as possible during the day—and turn the pigs into the yard to root it up, turn it over, and eat any scraps of kale or other food which the cows may have lost among the straw, or passed only partially digested in their dung.

To improve the quality of the compost that will be made from the farmyard manure, occasionally sprinkle sawdust, soil, ground lime-stone, in the yards, so that the cows may start the process of mixing and activating the compost before it goes out to the heaps.

JANUARY: 3rd Week

January is the time to *serve cows and heifers* to calve in October. Running a young bull with heifers is the best means of getting autumn calvers. There will be no record of services, but you will be more certain of getting the animals in calf. Service is generally achieved during the night and would be missed if the bull were not continuously with the heifers.

The only danger of service of this kind is at calving time, where no service date is known. It means that an extremely careful watch must be kept for animals threatening to calve—from nine months after the bull joined the heifers until ten months after he left them.

JANUARY: 4th Week

During the winter months milking cows are undergoing a great strain, producing milk from a ration which is unnatural. Heavy yielding cows should be watched for signs of trouble in the udder. All cows should be allowed an adequate ration of bulky green food. Indeed, the practice of giving priority to concentrated food and *filling up* on bulky food only after the concentrates have been fed, has done more to bring on udder and breeding troubles than any other method of management. I don't suggest that the animal should be stuffed with straw at the expense of more nutritive foods. But the cow is a ruminant and needs ample bulky food to assist digestion. Foodstuffs like silage and kale provide bulk as well as nutrition, and should therefore be given first importance.

The so-called production ration should, as far as possible, be home grown and made up of oats, linseed and/or beans. A simple production ration may be made up of three parts by weight of ground oats, with one part by weight of ground linseed and/or beans. This is a lower protein percentage than is generally advocated but better for the health of the cattle and not such a great strain on digestive and milk-secreting organs.

The linseed is particularly valuable medicinally, in view of its high oil and vitamin content. Keep your own linseed to grind. Linseed cake, which is the husk with its oil extracted, is a poor substitute for the whole linseed, though if you have to buy, it is the next best thing.

FEBRUARY: 1st Week

Because of the difficulty of 'spinning out' the winter rations, there is always a temptation to leave young stock short in order to get maximum milk yields from the herd. But young stock should be fed *more* lavishly during this month, otherwise they will lose condition. Though they may not show it externally for another month or two, if the food is stinted now, they will begin to 'melt' the inner layer of fat, and no amount of feeding will restore it satisfactorily once it is lost.

This does not mean that young stock should be fattened. They should be kept in a healthy growing condition, mainly with good hay (tripodded, if possible), silage and kale, with oat straw to fill up.

Newly weaned calves will need oats and linseed in the proportion, two parts linseed to three parts oats, up to the age of six months, fed at the rate of approximately 2 percent of the animal's live weight. That means, a calf of 150 1b. live weight will need 3 lb. a day of meal mixture.

Over six months of age, the proportion of linseed may be reduced to one linseed to three oats; and over twelve months, the animal will thrive entirely on hay, silage, kale, roots; or grass supplemented with one of these.

If there is an unlimited quantity of really first-class tripod hay or silage, or both, then young stock may be fed on them to the exclusion of all other foods. Best quality silage or hay is, of course, the nearest we can get to the natural food of the weaned animal, but it must be the best. The usual sun-scorched or rain-bleached hay will not do. Nor will coarse, overheated or sour silage.

FEBRUARY: 2nd Week

February sees the start of springtime activity on the farm, and everything should be done to get land ready for March sowings.

As the kale and root ground is cleared it should at once be disced. On heavy land it is possible to disc when you can't plough. Avoiding ploughing will enable you to get ahead quickly and gain time for other operations. The land is clean and easily worked after roots. Twice over with disc harrows should make the land just right for spring corn or linseed.

If spring wheat is to be sown it should have first preference. Wheat needs longer in the ground than any other cereal crop. Best varieties of spring wheat are Atle and Bersee, for sowing up to the end of March. If the crop can be got in now one of the winter varieties may be sown—such as Holdfast, Yeoman or Welcome, for land in good heart, or Little Joss, for poor or light land, though the yield will be much lighter than an autumn sowing.

S.172, S.147, and Marvellous oats may be sown up to the end of February. After that date it is better to use a true spring variety, such as

133

Star, Sun II, Yielder or Eagle. Spratt Archer, Plumage Archer or Abed Kenia are good barleys for sale; for feeding purposes, on strong land, Camton is a good cropper. See page 138 for further details.

Watch carefully for cows that are 'bulling' if you want winter milk. For the heat period is so short as to pass unnoticed unless the cows are closely examined daily. A drop in milk yield or a softening and reddening of the cow's vulva will make it worth while trying the bull on her if you want to get her served now.

FEBRUARY: 3rd Week

Besides the preparation of fields for spring cereal crops, the field in which the kale and roots are to be grown needs to be prepared this month. Every effort should be made to get at least part of the root land ready in time to sow the kale in March, so that the attack of the turnip fly will be avoided and also so that some early kale may be ready for feeding in August and September should a summer drought shorten the grass grazing season. The bulk of the kale crop need not, however, be sown until June or there will be too much stem and not enough leaf.

Compost which was left over from the previous spring or summer should be used up, and any compost that was made in the late summer or early autumn should now be ready to go out. If you haven't enough compost to cover all the root ground, get hold of some sewage sludge from your nearest town. Eight to ten tons an acre of raw sewage sludge will give a good start, but it must be kept on top—just disced in lightly—to allow aerobic bacterial action to break it down. Avoid sludge from towns with factories using chemicals. Alternatively, pay a little more and get some from one of the firms marketing sewage manure—1 or 2 tons an acre of the dried sewage powder will suffice until you can get some bulky compost on.

Ploughing. If any ploughing is done, use a subsoiling attachment on your plough. Though on all except grass land, especially on the lighter soils, it should be possible to prepare a satisfactory seed-bed with disc harrows only. Make sure that weeds are well killed on top before sowing.

Potatoes. Sell any remaining potatoes from the clamp, or at least see that any bad potatoes in the clamp are not damaging good ones.

Early Cattle Grazing. In the south, prepare to put the cows on to forward winter wheat and oats. As soon as there is enough growth for the cows to put their tongues around, put them to graze it or the wheat will grow away from them.

FEBRUARY: 4th Week

In all parts of the country the early sown winter corn should be almost ready for grazing, unless the winter has been a hard one. Graze down hard all crops that are dry enough to carry cows. Put the heifers on the damper fields—they will not do so much damage.

To graze all winter corn is equal to a light dressing of manure. It will encourage root development and increase the area from which the plant will draw its nutriment.

Early Bite. If the weather is frosty it is a good plan to put a light covering of straw, any kind, on the first grass field to be grazed. This will keep the soil warm and encourage early growth and give you just as early a bite as your neighbour who wastes his money on sulphate of ammonia, nitro-chalk or nitrate of soda.

Serve cows and heifers to calve in November. You will still need to have the bull running with heifers, if you are to be sure not to miss any during the night, as the heat period at this time is of extremely short duration, especially in a heifer.

MARCH: 1st Week

March is the month for cleaning weedy fields, and the opportunity is taken on the orthodox farm to pull out and rake up couch grass (or wicks, twitch, scutch, as it is variously known in different parts of the country). This is usually burnt; but this is an unnecessary waste of good organic matter, and time; it should be carried to the compost heap where no harm will come from mixing it through the heap in thin layers, provided the heap is built lightly enough to admit ample air for the development of heat. The heat, and later the earthworms and soil organisms, will completely change the nature of the small nodules which give rise to the numerous shoots from the underground roots of couch grass, and make it impossible for them to grow again.

Winter-sown wheat should be harrowed after being grazed by the cattle, to break the surface cake which will have formed over the soil as a result of winter rains, followed by drying winds. This should be done with light tooth harrows. The vigorous action of the tooth harrow does no serious damage to the young wheat plants, but is equivalent to earthing up and encourages them to 'tiller'—that is to put out numerous extra shoots from the base of the plant.

The Bull should be having a daily walk. It will do the herdsman good, too. Twenty minutes a day on a hard road will be the best investment you can make for your herd if you value your bull. It will increase his active life by years and keep him sweet-tempered, as well as keeping his feet in good trim. A bull with overgrown toes or weak legs or feet cannot work effectively.

Spread dung droppings on the grass fields whenever possible. This may seem a tedious task, but it well repays every minute spent. For on the average farms tons of grass and clover are lost each year where the rank growth around each dung patch is left ungrazed by the cattle. Even topping off with the mowing machine, though it is good for the rest of the field, does not make the growth around the dung more palatable, for even the fresh growth is left unconsumed until all the dung has completely disappeared—which will be a matter of two or three years. The reason for the refusal of cattle to eat rank grass is the excess of nitrogen in the dung, indicating how distasteful to the cattle is a crop forced with manure excessively nitrogenous, and also the grazing animals' instinctive defence against parasitic worms.

MARCH: 2nd Week

Where weed-covered stubbles have been used for winter grazing, the young cattle should now be moved out to pastures or winter corn. A good plan is to allow them to follow up the cows. It is surprising how well dry cows and young stock will clear up the coarse grazing left by milking cows.

Every opportunity to prepare land for spring-sown crops should now be taken. Any field that is weedy will now be showing its spring growth of green weeds and should be given frequent working with the disc harrow if the heifers have finished grazing it. All fields will be bare except those that are now being cleared of kale or carry winter crops. Most of them will have been disced during the winter to germinate and kill weed seedlings. (A final working to kill these weeds and leave them on the surface as manure will now be beneficial before sowing the crops.)

Seed-beds will need to be finer at this time of year, as there will be few frosts to crumble the lumps. The finer the seed-bed the quicker the germination, provided there is adequate organic matter on the surface to hold moisture for use at the proper time.

It is worth while spending an extra few days working the land into a fine tilth even if the crops are sown that much later, rather than to sow them in a rough knobbly seed-bed in which a proportion of the seed will not germinate.

Don't be tempted to speed the growth of that late field with artificial nitrogen or superphosphates; a light top dressing from the churned-up weeds on the surface will do far more good and last longer in its nutritional effect on the crop.

MARCH: 3rd Week

Sow spring cereals at the following rates, in the soils indicated, according to fertility:

Soil	Barley	Oats	Wheat	Rate cwt. p.a.
High	Camton	Star	Bersee	$1\frac{1}{2}$
Fertility	Pioneer	Eagle	Atle	,,
	Abed Kenia	Sun II		,,
Medium	Camton	Onward	Bersee	,,
Fertility	Spratt Archer	Marvellous	Atle	,,
	Abed Kenia	Yielder	Fylgia	,,
	Plumage			
	Archer	Sun II		,,
Low	Spratt Archer	Victory	Red Marvel	2
Fertility		Ardri	April	,,
		Black	Bearded	,,
		Tartary		

The best variety of spring wheat for all soils is Atle, which may be sown at any time from September to March—the earlier the better. For medium to strong soils, Bersee is the heaviest yielder, though not such a good milling variety.

Wheat should at this time of year be sown at the rate of $1\frac{1}{2}$ cwt. per acre, though more may be sown if the state of fertility and the fineness of seed-bed are not good.

Drill with any kind of corn seed drill, and follow the drill with one stroke of the light tooth harrow. In a very dry time it is a help to capillary action and water retention to roll after the harrow, though, as humus content increases as a result of fertility farming methods, the moisture will take care of itself and rolling will not be necessary.

If a large amount of organic trash remains on the surface soil, the seed will have to be sown broadcast and covered afterwards with the disc harrow offset at a shallow angle. Some old hands can make a quicker and better job by hand broadcasting, though there are few such skilled men on our farms today.

As the years of following the methods of this book progress a great saving in seed will be possible. I can grow a heavy crop of wheat on my soil with 1 cwt. of seed—wheat or oats—per acre, due to the improved condition of the soil.

See that all machinery is in good order for haymaking and harvesting. Grease and oil all wearing parts and check on every part which is subject to strain. If the implements needing repair were not taken in during the autumn or winter, which is the right time for such repairs, see that they go now or the mechanic will be too busy to do your job when you need the implement.

MARCH: 4th Week

All cereals except barley and linseed should have been sown by now. But barley and linseed may with success be left until April *if necessary*, though the earlier the sowing the better the yield is likely to be. Barley and linseed both need a very fine seed-bed, especially if they are sown late.

Sow barley at the rate of $1\frac{1}{2}$ to 2 cwt. an acre, according to the fertility of the soil, and choose one of the varieties listed on page 138.

Linseed varieties used for feeding purposes are Royal and Redwing. Sow with an ordinary corn drill at the rate of 50 to 60 lb. an acre, according to fertility and fineness of seed-bed.

Cover the linseed with the chain harrows or, if it is very dry, a roller.

If the cattle have been grazing winter cereals it will have been a good introduction to the spring grass. But in any case the cows should be introduced to the spring grass now ready in most parts of the country.

Divide the grass into small paddocks and graze alternately.

Cows for winter calving should be served now. This is a good month for turning a young bull out with heifers, which will then calve from December onwards.

If cows are being introduced to a new ley after the winter feeding, a twenty-four-hour fast is valuable before they go to the ley to help clear out residues of winter concentrates which may remain undigested in the stomach to set in motion the fermentation with clover which gives rise to 'Bloat.' If you don't fast the cows, as a precaution, and some get blown, then fast for twenty-four hours as a cure, giving a little charcoal—or charcoal tablets available from herbal firms. See page 212 for chapter on Bloat—its prevention and treatment. See Appendix for herbal supplies.

MARCH: 5th Week

Notice the speed with which early-sown cereal crops are germinating and growing on the unploughed fields. They are taking full advantage of being sown shallowly in their natural surroundings of organic matter left on top from the previous crop residues and weeds.

And even at this early stage heavy rains will be more readily absorbed by the topsoil. Walk over ploughed land and land worked only with the disc harrow, and compare the feel.

APRIL: 1st Week

Winter Greens. Kale should now be sown for use in the autumn and land prepared for potatoes. Don't waste time and labour on mangolds.

Kale is best sown on the flat. The rate of seeding will be as follows: kale (drilled) 4 lb. an acre; kale (broadcast) 10 lb. an acre.

Early Potatoes. In the south of England it is a matter of choice whether potatoes are sown before the other roots, or vice versa. In the North late frosts are the governing factor. In any case, early potatoes should be planted now at the rate of 1 ton an acre. Plant them on the surface and well cover with compost or farmyard manure, to be earthed up slightly when the green leaves have grown. See page 49.

Otherwise, well-rotted manure or compost should be carted to the kale and potato field as soon as possible, and spread at the rate of 15 tons an acre of well-rotted manure, or 10 tons an acre of compost.

APRIL: 2nd Week

With all spring crops sown, and even between the intervals of preparing land and sowing, especially when weather prevents other work, the spring compost heaps should be built. Manure which has accumulated in the yards, or which has been carted into temporary heaps during the winter, should be carted out in the spring and incorporated with all other dry vegetable waste to produce compost for use in the autumn. Trim hedges, ditches and banks for materials—now or whenever convenient.

Making Compost. For detailed instructions, see page 91.

If time permits, build the heap where it is to be used. Whenever you go to town with van or lorry, bring back a load of sewage sludge, sawdust or shavings, for use in and on the compost heap; then, not only will the sawdust or sewage sludge be free, but so will the transport.

Scour the town for any other organic waste which may be going—spent hops, shoddy, old sacks, greengrocers' refuse, etc.

GREEN MANURING

Undersow cereal crops with 8 lb. Italian ryegrass, 4 lb. trefoil, for autumn grazing and subsequent green manuring. Even better results will follow if up to 8 lb. trefoil are used, but be guided by your pocket at this stage—the thicker the legume sward the better the effect on the cover crop and subsequent soil fertility.

APRIL: 3rd Week

The temporary grass mixtures may be sown this month, as early as possible, though I prefer sowing on stubble after harvest. As the cows finish grazing the winter oats, harrow the field with the fixed tooth harrow and thereby obtain a covering of loose soil. The seed may then be sown at any time; though preferably on a day that is not too windy to cause broadcast seed to fall unevenly.

The mixture should include a good proportion of the coarser grasses and herbs, which are in any case natural to the ruminant, but have been absent from her diet since man started to grow grass as a cultivated crop. Such troubles in the dairy herd as bloat and sterility have increased with the development of the ley and the simplification of the mixture. I have almost eliminated bloat since my leys included herbs and coarse grasses, and milk yields have not suffered. See page 47 for mixtures.

In undersowing grass and clover seeds broadcast, it is difficult to see where the seed has fallen. It is necessary, therefore, to put sticks up across the field and move them at each crossing of the field to the extent of the width to which the seed fiddle will sow. The same procedure is also necessary with the seed barrow.

As soon as good weather comes the cows may be turned out at nights.

APRIL: 4th Week

Sugar Beet

The last two weeks in April are considered to be the best time for sowing sugar beet, though a number of farmers have had improving results by sowing earlier than the formerly accepted end of April sowing. It is well, however, to begin sowing if there is any considerable acreage, and extend if necessary until the first week in May. At least there will be a margin of time in case of hold-ups. Soak the seed in water for two nights before sowing. This will speed germination and give a quicker get-away from the weeds. Rate of seeding is 12 to 14 lb. an acre, or more in poor soil.

Lucerne

The livestock farmer should not be without a piece of lucerne for the purpose of making silage or cutting green for cattle food during a period of drought.

Don't worry about weeds—they will be eliminated after one or two cuts have been taken. This applies to most weeds so long as they are not too thick to prevent proper establishment of the lucerne. Compost should be applied just before, or at the time of sowing, unless it has been applied for one of the two previous crops. Unless the soil has a very high organic content the seed should be dressed with a culture obtainable from the seed supplier.

Seed should be sown not later than the end of April or else left until July.

Sown alone it should be at the rate of 25 lb. an acre, which may be drilled in the ordinary way, though 16 lb. of lucerne with 3 lb. of timothy or cocksfoot will give better results.

MAY: 1st Week

Few farms will have got all the kale sown and preparation should be made for a further sowing in early May, with the addition of swedes

142

and turnips if they are likely to be needed. It is well to have a succession of various roots and green food to keep the cattle going from September until the cows go out to grass, day and night, next April or May.

Swedes should be sown at the rate of 4 1b. an acre; turnips 3 lb. an acre in drill. Turnips may also be sown broadcast at three times that seeding, for folding on sheep or cattle to eat mainly the green tops. For this purpose turnips may be sown at any time up to the end of August.

AUTUMN SILAGE CROP

Sow oats and vetches for cutting green after harvest if you need to make autumn silage. Ideal proportions are $1\frac{1}{2}$ bushels vetches to $1\frac{1}{2}$ bushels oats, though more or less vetches may be sown, according to the price of seed and the bulkiness of crop required. The vetches provide the greatest bulk, so the more vetch seed up to 2 bushels the better. Oats and vetches are the best arable silage mixture, the oats being sown for the purpose of supporting the vetches which have a creeping tendency. Ten to 12 tons of silage should be got from each acre of a $1\frac{1}{2}$ by $1\frac{1}{2}$ mixture.

Cattle should be taken off all autumn-sown cereals, though there has been no harm in grazing them continuously until now. If a dry season seems likely, get them off in the third week of April. In the North too, where recovery is not so quick, mid-April is late enough. Fields that have been grazed should be harrowed with fixed tooth harrows immediately the cattle have left them.

Proceed with compost making, particularly in wet weather.

Serve cows and heifers to calve in February.

MAY: 2nd Week

CATTLE OUT

All except the youngest livestock should now be going out day and night, and grass should be grazed hard, as from now on it will tend to grow away from the cattle. It is almost impossible to overstock grass land during the months of May and June, and full advantage should be taken of this lush growing season during which the cows need no indoor feeding at all. Good ley grazing should provide for up to four gallons of milk daily during May and June.

Opportunities should be taken now to tidy up the accumulations of winter should this not have been done before. The time is rapidly approaching when there will be no time for trimmings, and farming will be a twenty-four hour a day job until after harvest. So clean up the yards; clean out the sheds on wet days; complete the compost heaps that will be needed for use in the autumn; turn compost heaps made in March, if there is a day when other productive work cannot be done. Turning compost will improve its finished quality, though, given normal weather conditions and a carefully made heap, it should not be necessary.

Examine fences around all pasture and ley fields. Straying cattle are a curse during busy summer, and now may be your last chance to make the fences stock-proof. There is usually only time for temporary patching during hay-time and harvest.

MAY: 3rd Week

MACHINERY CHECK

Make a final check up on all the machinery likely to be needed in the summer. Spare parts for the harvest machinery should have been ordered in the winter, but in any case do it now if you don't want to be held up at the busiest time of the year.

On wet days take the opportunity to whitewash the insides of farm buildings now that they are empty.

If mangolds and sugar beet have been sown, they will now need constant hoeing, and as soon as they have reached an individually identifiable size they should be singled out to a distance of about 9 to 12 inches apart. If only a matter of an inch or so separates a weak plant that might be left and a strong one, you would, for the sake

144

of even spacing cut out, always leave the stronger plant rather than attempt to be too exact about spacing.

Land that has not been ploughed this year, and which was cropped after only surface cultivation, particularly if compost and not farmyard manure was used, will not suffer greatly from weeds—and the few that will remain in the field can be regarded as good companionship for the domestic crop. Don't worry unduly about a few weeds so long as they don't smother out the crop. Just keep them under control. See Chapter 6 on Weeds.

MAY: 4th Week

Silage Making

Green crops sown in the early autumn for the purpose of silage will now be ready for cutting. At least a start should be made as soon as there is a growth of about a foot in height, otherwise the crop will grow too coarse before the field is finished.

From now on silage making should go on steadily each day, starting with the arable green crop, such as oats and vetches, and going on to the lucerne and the clover ley.

A pit silo dug out of the soil is the most satisfactory, and the green crop may be carted into the pit if sloping ramp-like ends are made, and the tractor or horse drawn over the silage to compact it.

Molasses is not essential in the making of silage, but it does improve the quality of the finished product by assisting the production of the organic acids which ensure the preservation of the crop. There is also considerable nutritive value in the crude molasses, particularly if it is from the sugar-cane and not the sugar beet.

Inorganic acids, such as are advocated in the system known as A.I.V., should *on no account be used* if the health of the stock is valued.

The object of making silage is to pack the green material so tightly that air is excluded and oxidation and decomposition thus prevented. Excessive soft, wet green material should be avoided, however, and this is best adjusted by ensuring that no water is used with the softer immature greenstuff, and that the temperature rises each day to a heat at which it is just impossible to hold the hand thrust into the silage for more than a few seconds.

11a. Tractor compressing silage in pit at Goosegreen.

11b. A seed crop of oats and vetches.

12a. A pit silo being dug out by tractor and earth scoop.

12b. Visitors watch the making of a silage pit at Goosegreen.

Work on two pits or silos on alternate days and fill them as quickly as possible.

If there is likely to be a few days' gap during the filling of a pit or silo, cover and weight the lot, or decomposition will cause much waste on the surface.

Silage preserves all the natural elements of grasses and clovers as nearly as is possible to their original state in a way which is not possible with any other winter food. Unlike dried grass, it calls for no expensive machinery, and what gives it supremacy as a winter food is the fact that cattle of all ages from calfhood prefer it to any other food—and, what is more, thrive on it, almost better than they do on grass!

Keep a patch of the oats and vetches to be harvested for seed purposes. Vetches are costly to buy, and it is easy to harvest them on tripods.

JUNE: 1st Week

GRASS AND CLOVER SILAGE

When the arable silage crop or lucerne is finished, make an early start on the clover ley. Work away, cutting as much grass each day as can be cleared up and put into the silage pit, and proceed on the assumption that the weather will never be fit for hay-making.

It is surprising what two or three men can get through in the way of silage making, working steadily day after day. It is important these days to manage without the need for augmenting the labour force for seasonal work. Silage making spreads the work for a small staff. Unlike hay, it does not need a large squad of men working at breakneck speed for a few days of fine weather. Rain or fine, the silage can be made each day, and if it is made during rainy weather added water is not needed. If a really fine spell of weather comes, then you may think of haymaking.

BLOAT OR HOVEN AND CONTROLLED GRAZING

Watch the cows for possible 'blowing.' Divide the grassland into small sections and leave the cows on continuously, rather than taking them into a large field for a short spell of grazing. I used to practise the modern idea of giving them only an hour or so morning and night on a large piece of lush ley; but this encourages the cows to gorge themselves, for they get to know they have only a limited time in which to fill their stomachs.

Left for the day on a good herbal ley, at the rate of about ten cows to the acre, they take their time over the grazing and graze the grass down evenly before passing on to the next paddock. It is possible by this means to keep them on fresh productive grass, and the frequent changes are beneficial to the cows, who are not happy to be in one field for more than two weeks at a time, their natural instinct being to roam to frequent fresh pastures.

The leys may be divided with an electric fence, hung on insulators screwed on to a leg of your haymaking tripods, erected at 10 to 12 yards apart—particularly if the fence is temporary. They are thus easily moved. This system is excellent for kale grazing where the fence is moved daily and when, of course, you will have plenty of tripods out of a job.

JUNE: 2nd Week

If you are short of space (and if you aren't, you should grow more or carry more stock), it is well to allow the dry and young stock to follow the cows around, to clear up the rougher grasses left behind by the cows; though, where acreage allows, keep the young stock in separate fields of their own.

Whichever system is practised, as soon as the paddock is grazed right down, spread the dung droppings carefully by hand, then with the chain harrows, otherwise by the time the cows come back to it coarse, sour patches will have grown up which will not be eaten by any of the stock. The aim should be to spread the droppings as evenly as possible over the field and thereby gain the fullest advantage from it. I have stressed the dung-spreading because if it isn't done carefully I find that on closely folded leys as much as a fifth of the acreage is wasted by the end of a grazing season because of rank growth which nothing will eat. It may seem to be a slow and wasteful business spreading it by hand, but apart from the new weeder attachment for the light integral power-unit tractors, there is no other way of ensuring even spreading.

If you have one of these tractors, it is worth getting the weeder solely for this job. Use it after topping off the ley with the mower.

If you are going to spread the dung spots at this time of year, right in the middle of your silage making, and with haymaking waiting on the weather, you will have no time for anything else.

JUNE: 3rd Week

If you are going to make any hay, the grass is now at its optimum nutritional value for this purpose. When the weather seems to be settled for a few days, stop making silage and cut as much grass as you can get on the tripods the same evening, or next morning in case of an exceptionally heavy crop. Use the tedder immediately after the mowing machine, and in a moderate crop build the tripod huts the same evening from the morning's cutting.

If the weather breaks, go on making silage again and don't worry about hay, for the grass is losing even less by being made into silage, no matter how coarse it has grown, than if it is made into hay. I make only enough hay for the very young stock, relying on tripodded oat straw, silage and kale for everything else.

Disc harrow the field from which the arable silage was made and continue throughout the summer if it is weedy and to be sown to a cereal crop in the autumn. Or, if it is really fertile, prepare it for sowing kale. If you can't get sludge or compost, kale cannot be sown on the poor field, so take the chance of a green-manuring crop, such as mustard, to be disced in before sowing the cereal crop.

If kale is intended, compost should have been spread in the autumn for the silage crop, and the soil will then be in ideal condition for quick preparation of a seed-bed and to receive the kale seed this month.

If the field had no compost get sewage sludge on quickly. Ten tons to the acre is a good dressing, and kale will romp away and laugh at the 'fly' if sown in this sludge after or just before rain, about this time of year.

JUNE: 4th Week

LATE KALE

If you have a patch of land on which late kale is to be sown, take every opportunity to 'bastard' fallow it; that is, to work it over with the disc harrow in order to kill any weeds that may grow.

If the field has not been manured, and the compost is in short supply, get on to your nearest local authority and ask permission to dig a few lorry loads of sewage sludge from the sewage works. This is first-class manure, though it may be a little unpleasant to handle. If you haven't a lorry of your own, it should be possible to hire one to do the whole job of carting and dropping it in heaps on the field at a price of about £1 a ton, depending on the distance of your farm from the sewage works.

An alternative source of humus is the dried sewage sludge which is marketed by a number of local authorities, notably Dartford Urban District Council, Leatherhead Rural District Council, Middlesex County Council, and others, as well as a number of commercial concerns, some of whom advertise in the farming Press.

Spread dung droppings in the grazing field.

Don't forget to visit daily any outlying stock. Young stock that are running out on fields away from the farm should never be missed. They are the most important part of the daily routine in the middle of haymaking. Wherever your cattle are, make a point of seeing them at least once a day.

JULY: 1st Week

This is a good time to sow kale. Kale sown now will need no hoeing and will miss the 'fly'. The field can be worked now and weeds killed by a few hours' strong sun. After a good shower of rain, with the soil warm and moist, the kale will germinate quickly and grow away in the unlikely event of late attacks of fly. Little weeding will be needed for kale sown on land un-ploughed this year, for if there have been opportunities to kill weeds on the surface there will be lit-

tle else left to grow. With no thinning, either, the kale will not interfere in any way with the busy harvest that is soon about to begin.

Bulls should be tethered out to grass, preferably some distance from
water. You should then insist on them being taken to water twice a day.
This will ensure the exercise which is so essential to a working bull. In
Cobbett's day, and earlier, the bull turned the cider press or the eleva-
tor, and provided a lot of motive power—now supplied by electricity
or stationary engines. Now we pay a man to take it for a walk and for
a machine to do its job—or, rather its spare-time job. The ideal place
for a bull is running with the herd, but if you wish to avoid summer
calvings, he should be restricted after the end of this month.

Collect from your supplier the binder twine that will be needed for
cutting corn.

Get your petrol, tractor vapourizing, or diesel oil tanks filled with
fuel ready for the harvest, so that hold-ups at critical times will be
avoided.

If it is possible to book extra labour for the harvest time, make the
necessary arrangements now.

<hr>

JULY: 2nd Week

<hr>

THATCH ALL HAYSTACKS NOW

Then take a few days off. Go to a few agricultural shows. Get married—if you haven't done so already. It is an essential part of successful farming, and now is the traditional time for this event in the farming
programme—between hay-time and harvest. If you just cannot leave
the place, and you need some work to pass away the time, trim a few
hedges, clean a few ditches; but, above all, be sure you are ready for
harvest. A spell of sunny weather will quickly ripen the winter oats
now.

Check over all harvesting machinery; see that the binder knotter is
in working order and that the knotter knife is sharp and free from rust.
Oil round the binder and see that all the leathers and buckles on the
canvases are strong and capable of a heavy season's cutting.

If you like to do a neat job in the harvest field you could start open-
ing out, i.e. cutting around the headlands of the cornfields while the
crop is still green, and use the greenstuff for silage or feeding green to

cattle in case of drought. This can be done with a mowing machine and will save the trouble of tying up sheaves of corn cut by scythe. Most farmers just drive into the field and go right round with the tractor and binder, trampling down a proportion of the crop; but there still are some who feel this wasteful and like to have a way cleared round the field before starting harvesting.

There is still time to sow some kale; the varieties hungry gap kale, thousand-headed kale, or rape kale would be best for late sowings. These varieties are leafy and yet frost resistant, and will give maximum yields in the early part of next year, when Marrow-stem kale would be past its best. Seeding rates are the same as for other small seeded root crops: 4 1b. an acre in drills or 8 to 10 lb. an acre broadcast.

JULY: 3rd Week

Turn the Compost if it has cooled down without getting crumbly and friable, but if ample air was incorporated when the heaps were built this should not have happened, and good compost will result without turning. But if you wish to have the fine crumbly material upon which many gardeners pride themselves, a turn of the heap will help to achieve this, and if weed seeds or couch grass were plentiful in the original material, turning is a wise precaution anyhow. In the process of turning, the dry outer material should be turned to the centre, and if the heap is too wet, as it well may be in the wetter parts of the West Country and the North, a little dry soil or sawdust incorporated in the mixing will be a good thing. If too dry, the heap should be moistened to the condition of a squeezed-out sponge. If sawdust is used and is not completely decomposed when the heap is used, be sure to keep the compost on top of the soil for best results.

Calves born during the summer may be left out day and night, if possible with their foster mothers. Not only is it more economical to rear calves naturally, for the calf needs less milk from the cow direct than via the bucket, but it is also healthier for the cow and the calf. A good plan is to allow the calf to have one quarter (a different one every day), or from an exceptional milker only a part of a quarter (so long as the calf gets about half a gallon daily from the cow), and milking the other three for purposes of selling. This is simple to work with hand-milked herds, but where a machine is employed it means attaching only three teat cups. However, give the system a trial, if only for the sake of the future health of your herd. Don't worry too much about your herd average. The day is fast coming when herd health will be far more important than excessive herd averages.

Watch outlying heifers and dry cows, and examine their udders for summer mastitis. If a case is suspected, bring the animal in and confine it without food until the inflammation is gone or the discharge is completely cleared. Instructions for the treatment of mastitis, after the immediate cessation of food, are on page 199. You may say good-bye to mastitis next year if you have got right over to fertility farming, except of course in old cows with a history of bad feeding.

On your Sunday strolls round the farm, compare the fields that have had compost with the rest of the farm. Already the worm population will be greater. Composted potatoes will resist blight—take a look for your own satisfaction—and they will be free of it in two or three years' time if you use only compost-grown seed.

JULY: 4th Week

LUCERNE SILAGE

An opportunity should occur just before the corn is ripe to take a cut of lucerne for silage or tripod hay. It may be necessary at this time of year to cut and cart a little lucerne daily to the cows to keep the milk yields going during a dry time on the grass, though with good herbal leys this problem will disappear as the organic top skin is built year by year.

At this time of year, particularly if the sun is hot, avoid cutting more lucerne than can be carried before it is scorched by the sun.

Continue when the opportunity presents itself to cultivate the 'bastard fallow'—the field from which the oat and vetch silage was taken, if it was not sown with green crop, so that it will be weed-free when the time comes to sow wheat.

BREAKING A LEY

If you wish to break a ley this summer, now is the time to plough it so that the grass sod can be turned under to commence decomposition. You may later, if you wish, plough again to bring the organic matter

13. Born in the field in early summer, these calves spend the rest of their lives out of doors.

14a. Cows grazing Winter wheat at Goosegreen in early March. Wheat is sown deliberately to provide winter and early spring grazing. (See 'Grazing Round the Calendar').

14b. Silage being used from the pit, the filling of which is illustrated on Plate 11a. Note absence of waste on top and sides in spite of incessant rain while in the pit 1950–51, though the pit was not covered in any way. Photograph taken January 1951.

back to the surface where it will most benefit the subsequent crop. The cows should be grazed hard for the weeks preceding ploughing on the ley that is to be broken. This will simplify the process of turning the turf under, without the need to plough so deep that the sod will putrefy. If left as near the surface as possible it will be broken down by oxygen-loving soil organisms.

If the field is an old thistly or nettly pasture, run the mower over before ploughing—and carry the material to the silage pit or the compost heap. It is well worth the trouble for either purpose—and will ease the task of preparing the seed-bed. In any case, these weeds are almost certain to have seeded by now and they are better carried away than left to seed in the first crop after the grass.

Give the root fields a final clean up before starting harvest. Hoe out any persistent thistles and hand-pull the docks.

AUGUST: 1st Week

HARVESTING OATS

Oats should be cut a little on the green side. The seed will not suffer and a greenish oat straw at the time of cutting will have a nutritional value approaching that of much of the hay that is made in England today.

If your staff is big enough you can keep the tractor and binder cutting one field after another while the rest of the staff follows on tripodding the corn as it is cut. Alternatively, it is better to cut one field at a time and get it tripodded before passing on to the next field.

The corn may be put on the tripods a few hours after cutting. If you are tripodding the cereals, the main aim should be to keep the sheaves as upright as possible around the tripod air vent and wires in building, and, as with the hay, keep the whole hut narrow and vertical sided.

The usual mistake in tripodding is to build the huts too big—with too many sheaves to each hut—about 100 average-sized sheaves is ideal. The old handstack method should not be imitated in making tripods. The technique is quite different and, as with hay, the aim should be to construct a narrow conical funnel, though the more like a tubular shell it is the better, to ensure rain 'run-off.'

GOING FERTILITY

The combine has its uses in a catchy season, like 1950, for harvesting a field on the one day that it is dry; but in a normal year I would prefer tripods, and if I owned or could hire a combine cheaply I would use it for threshing in the field from the tripods. I value the straw far too much to allow it to get overripe or wasted, as is the tendency with the combine—to say nothing of the criminal practice of burning straw after the combine.

AUGUST: 2nd Week

Once the corn is on tripods it is perfectly safe for the rest of the winter. All it needs if it is to be left out for more than a few weeks is a topping of straw and a piece of string to hold it down in case of high winds. I have threshed for seed purposes linseed that has been out all the winter without a grain of waste. Others have done the same with oats and barley on a large scale.

If you use tripods for your hay and cereals, and make silage of the rest, you can count your weather worrying days over, as far as harvesting winter fodder is concerned. And if you are going to crop your land this coming autumn without ploughing it, you will have your land cropped and growing before your less enlightened neighbour has found a suitable day on which to work his land.

With your corn on tripods you can go for a few trips to summer shows without worrying about the fact that your corn is still out. If the field is undersown don't worry about damage to the clover. I have left tripod huts on a ley for a month without damage, and if the building has been properly carried out the main weight will be carried by the tripod wires.

Don't neglect the cows because you are in the midst of harvest. See that they are being moved on to a new grazing paddock as soon as they have taken off the best of the one now in use. If the dry weather has stopped the growth of grass, make a point of cutting some green crop for them. If the lucerne is not at the cutting stage there should be good growth on the autumn silage crop of oats and vetches sown in April. You score now if you have made early silage, for if you have already made enough for your winter requirements you can be lavish with the green crop now at a time when milk yields often drop badly for want of good green food.

Judge the ripeness of your cereal crop as follows:

OATS

Before the straw is yellow all the way up, while there is still a good amount of green in it, take one of the grains from the ear and squeeze it. If it has a firm husk and a clotted cream centre it is fit to cut. Another test is to see the oat grain beginning to show from the chaff in the head of the oat. But this stage should be anticipated by a few days if you wish to get the fullest value from the straw.

WHEAT

When squeezed the grain should be the consistency of cream cheese. If left much beyond this the grain will fall out of the ear during stooking and carrying. It does not matter if the straw has a slightly green tinge in patches. These will ripen off as soon as the wheat is in a stook.

AUGUST: 3rd Week

Wheat does not suffer from the ill effects of rain like the other cereal crops, and if you haven't enough tripods wheat is the crop for which they are not so essential. Even during showery weather, provided the soil is not too wet to enable the binder to travel, wheat may be cut soon after rain stops, and a gentle breeze blows off the superficial moisture from the straw. Also, unless continuous pouring rains are experienced for days on end, there will be no appreciable damage from leaving the wheat out in the stook. The stiff straw allows the rain to run off quickly, which makes it possible to carry wheat to the stack, if necessary, very soon after a shower.

SPROUTING PRECAUTIONS

If you have grown Holdfast wheat, however, because it is one of the best milling varieties, it is also the quickest to sprout in the stook. Care should be taken, therefore, to get this cut and carried as quickly as possible. It is even better to cut it a little on the unripe side if the weather is really good and get it safely under cover as soon as the grain is hard and the straw is dry.

When wheat is dead ripe and the weather is settled, at any rate in the south of England, and often in the north, it is possible to carry it to the stack without stooking or tripodding. But it needs a very good judge of weather and the condition of the wheat to do this.

Oats, on the other hand, should be left out to mature in the tripod for a couple of weeks. The 'old-timers' tell us to leave it in stook for three Sundays to be on the safe side.

Stacking (assuming you have not threshed from tripods in the field).

The test of the readiness for grain crops to be stacked is to thrust your hand down into the middle of the sheaf into the part where the sheaf is tied. If the straw is brittle, and quite dry inside, it is safe to carry it, assuming at the same time that the heads of grain are perfectly dry. A little surface dampness resulting from a slight shower need not deter you from getting on with the carrying, especially in a busy time.

AUGUST: 4th Week

It will not be possible to thresh every field without stacking some of the crop—even from the tripod, as the field will be needed for cultivation or grazing—so some stacking is generally necessary.

STACKING

It is surprising how few experienced farmers are really expert stackers—capable of building stacks that will withstand all weathers—even without thatching.

In building a stack, start by building a stook in the middle and encircle the stook with sheaves of corn each covered by the other up to the tying string in the middle of the sheaf, fanwise, heads towards the centre, until the previously marked-out perimeter of the stack is reached. Then place the sheaves round and round the stack, butt outwards, placing each course up to the string of the previous course of sheaves. When the middle is reached each time, fill it in above the level of the rest of the stack and keep the middle always slightly higher, so that all sheaves are sloping very slightly downwards. This will mean that any rain falling on the outside of the stack will tend to run off rather than to run down the straw into the stack, as would happen if the sheaves were tilted inwards.

THATCHING

If thatching seems to be out of pace with the times, and you wish to effect a quick coverage of corn stacks not already under the barn, sheaves of wheat straw may be pinned on the stack to form a rain-proof roof. Thatching spars, or any kind of sharp-pointed stick, may be used for this purpose.

Thatching, which is still the best way of achieving rain-proof stacks, if they are not to be threshed for a long time, cannot be taught on paper. Spend a day on the stack with one of the few remaining 'old-timers'— if you wish to learn thatching.

Now is a good time to sow down a ley on the disced stubble without ploughing. If at all acid spread ground limestone. Sow the mixture on page 49, see Appendix for suppliers. Drag afterwards with light drag harrows or disc again if rough, but very lightly or the discs will put the seed too deep.

Leys may be sown from now until the third week of September.

AUGUST: 5th Week

Barley and linseed are usually ready for cutting after the oats and wheat are finished. Barley is left until it is dead ripe and the ears are drooping. Linseed is ready to cut when the seed inside the boll turns pale brown in colour and the straw is nearly changed from green to golden. The cutting of barley is straightforward, but the linseed will need a little special application to the work if it is to run smoothly.

The binder knife should be razor sharp, and a sharpened knife should be kept in readiness for frequent changes if any considerable acreage of linseed is to be cut. The new serrated-edged knife is the ideal for cutting linseed. If any difficulty is experienced in cutting examine the straw of the linseed to see which is the toughest part of its stem and adjust your knife accordingly. The part nearest the root, just above the ground level, is usually the toughest portion, and improved cutting may be obtained by raising the bed of the binder slightly to a more tender part of the stem.

Linseed in stook or tripod suffers very little from the rain. So get on with carrying the other grain crops and leave the linseed until last.

Likewise with beans, which should be cut when the scar on the end of the bean, where it joins the pod, is black in colour. Once in stook, occasional rain does no serious harm because of the 'run-off' from the hard straw or haulm.

If there is any hold-up in carrying the grain crop, have the discs or cultivator ready to go into any field which has been cleared, and work the surface in order to germinate any weed seeds which may have fallen. You may even work between the rows of stooks in fields that have not been cleared if there appears to be a threat of long delays due to bad weather. The sooner weed seeds can be encouraged to germinate the sooner may the field be sown to autumn crops after harvest or be available for autumn grazing.

CHAPTER FIFTEEN

Which Breed?

W ith increased emphasis on pedigree to-day, and an increasing realization of its value among dairy farmers, many men who farm for a living are turning to the building of pedigree herds. But where is the necessary information which will enable them to decide which breed is the most suitable for the conditions under which they are farming?

The only statistics that are available, showing comparisons of the breeds under equal conditions, are those produced by farmers themselves, and these cannot be taken as authentic; few farmers have the cash or the scope to carry out the comparative costings that are required on a sufficiently large scale or over a sufficiently long period of time. This is surely a task for the County Farm Institutes or the new Ministry of Agriculture Experimental Farms.

If a farmer is growing wheat for the first time on a particular type of soil, and is doubtful regarding the most suitable variety to grow, all the information he requires will be supplied by his county agricultural organizer, backed by the results of experimental wheat plots which in most cases have been carried on for years. *If such information can be provided for seed varieties, why not for breed varieties?*

When I decided to change over from a mixed herd of non-pedigree animals to a pedigree herd of purely dairy breed, I could find no official information which would help in the choice of a breed best suited to my farm. So I had to set about sorting all the conflicting claims of the various breeders and breed societies, and finally landed nowhere. I was determined to be open-minded, but could find no one who could produce convincing evidence for the superiority of any one breed.

So my only course was to try out as many as possible on my farm. This I did long enough to satisfy myself as to the best breed for my circumstances.

Curiously, the breed which I finally chose, the Jersey, was the one against which I had been most prejudiced by the sources from which I gained information on the relative merits of the breeds.

But my experiments cannot claim to have any authenticity, and though I kept the best of three breeds, and continued the costings over an extended period before I reached my own decision, there is need for extensive and official trials of this kind.

At the present time the only guides for would-be pedigree breeders are milk yield and butterfat records. The average farmer to-day, failing authoritative comparative costings, tends to choose the breed which shows most consistently the highest milk records. But total yield means nothing unless it is related to cost of production.

It is surely better farming to keep two 750-gallon cows producing milk at a cost of 1s. a gallon than one 1,500 gallon-cow producing milk at a cost of 1s. 6d. a gallon. The difference in profit on milk alone would be considerable, to say nothing of the value of the extra calf in a pedigree herd. It is only on evidence such as this, of which there seems to be remarkably little available, that anyone can claim superiority for any single breed.

What we need are demonstration farms, at least one in each county, where the accepted dairy breeds—Ayrshire, Friesian, Shorthorn, Guernsey, Jersey, and possibly introductions from other countries such as the Brown Swiss—are kept side by side and costed in every detail, from birth through the producing life to death, generation after generation. The information we require should not be confined to the producing life of the cow, but should include: the cost of rearing each animal from birth to her first calf (for in this respect the early maturing breeds would start producing milk with a nine-months' advantage), the amount and cost of production ration required to produce every gallon of milk, and the cost of maintenance in milk and while dry.

These items shown separately would help farmers in the choice of different breeds for different systems of farming. But the most important figures, and the only figures capable of showing the true cost per gallon of milk production, would be the total cost of feeding the cows from birth to death, and the total lifetime production.

But even if such trials are started at once, it will be years before the authorities could issue really convincing results. What is the farmer, particularly the young enthusiast, of which fortunately there are an increasing number today, to do in the meantime?

WHICH BREED?

Many herds are in the position from which I started to build my pedigree herd; that is, with a mixed herd of one or two breeds and the crosses of these breeds.

It is my experience that there are considerable differences in the cost per gallon of milk production by the various breeds. Every farmer, then, who has not sunk himself too deeply into one breed, and who wishes to be satisfied that he is farming to the best of his farm's ability, would gain valuable information from small-scale costings on his dairy herd.

WHY I CHOSE THE JERSEY

I was reared on North Country dairy Shorthorns and started farming with a good commercial herd of Shorthorns. It is natural, then, that I should have had a strong prejudice against the Jersey breed until the purchase of two cheap first-calf heifers for the house demonstrated to me the amazing ability of these little animals to convert food into milk at a remarkably low cost.

I bought a few more and proceeded to keep careful records of food consumption in relation to milk production of the three breeds which I then had—Shorthorn, Friesian, and the crosses of these two—compared with the Jersey.

As the following figures indicate, I needed nothing more to convince me that I should be a fool to continue with breeds which put flesh on their ribs instead of milk into the bucket while milk production was my business.

Name of Cow	Breed	Yield	Cost per gallon			
		lb.	s.	d.	£*	$*
Annabelle	Shorthorn	$9,819\frac{2}{3}$	1	3	1.54	$2.83
Prosperous 2nd	Shorthorn x Friesian	} $8,368\frac{1}{2}$	1	6	1.85	$3.40
Beauty	Shorthorn x Friesian	} 17,256	1	0	1.23	$2.26
Prosperous	Friesian	13,808	1	4	1.65	$3.04
Fair Aldan	Jersey	$11,721\frac{1}{2}$		7	0.72	$1.33
June Rose (heifer)	Jersey	$8,002\frac{3}{4}$		$8\frac{1}{2}$	0.87	$1.60
Poppy ,,	Jersey	8,733		$7\frac{1}{2}$	0.77	$1.42
Yetanother ,,	Jersey	8,890		8	0.82	$1.51

Editor's note: The author's historic financial data was converted to modern currencies and approximately adjusted for inflation, using the consumer price index. This most certainly will not correlate to modern costs and prices, but should be utilized for general directional trends only.

It should be noted that these costs were calculated in 1945 when prices were considerably lower than they are to-day.

Since I changed over completely to the Jersey, and have built up over the past nine years a self-contained herd which averages over 800 gallons of 5.5 percent butterfat milk each on mainly home-grown food, I have discovered the following undeniable reasons why the Jersey is the dairy farmer's best commercial proposition under any conditions.

The Jersey, unlike almost any other breed of dairy cow except perhaps the Kerry, has not suffered from exploitive methods of management. Until recently, that is, almost right up to 1939, with few exceptions, the Jersey farmer has practised a balanced system of farming and has fed his cows naturally with no attempt to extract excessive yields of milk. Only one or two of the larger herds concentrated on milk yield, and even then not at the expense of butterfat and type. Similarly, in this country, the Jersey was in the hands of breeders who considered high milk yields unimportant, for in view of the Jersey's inability to convert food to body fat she was always, in any case, an economical and efficient producer. Consequently, the majority of Jerseys have an inheritance of comparative health and sound constitution.

My animals live almost entirely out of doors, and under such conditions the Jersey grows a thick shaggy protective coat which retains body heat in winter.

The Jersey is early maturing and will produce a calf and 700 or so gallons of milk before most other breeds calve down, though it is wise not to stick too strictly to the recommended bulling age for the breed which is fifteen months (to calve the first calf at two years old). I have them bulled at from fifteen to twenty months old, according to growth and general condition.

Longevity is a valuable characteristic of the Jersey, and this again is due to the freedom from exploitation and artificial feeding almost right up to 1940, in the Jersey breed. Given a reasonably natural existence, especially with regard to rearing and feeding, the Jersey will produce economically and breed consistently up to the age of fourteen to twenty. I have a number of cattle between those ages, and one now aged twenty-one, that great cow Lockyers Verbena, bred by Mr. John G. Bell, which is the oldest living pedigree cow in this country. I expect all my home-bred cattle to serve me efficiently up to the age of twenty.

The Jersey is supreme as a producer of butterfat, a fact which I am convinced is due to the extensive use of seaweed in manuring the soil of Jersey, and the ability to convert all food to butterfat rather than body fat.

The fact that I, and many other milk producers, foresaw the approaching era of consumer discrimination made me prepare for the day when only milk of high butterfat content will meet a ready sale. The time is near when it will be impossible to sell anything but Channel Island milk, except for manufacture at lower prices. The disqualifications at the London Dairy Show of 1950 is the writing on the wall. Seventeen Friesians, one Ayrshire, and one Red Poll were disqualified because their milk contained less than the legal requirement of fat or solids-not-fat. I asked the breed societies concerned how they explained this considerable decline in milk quality, and they had to admit it was due to the modern concentration on excessive yields regardless of quality.

If ever I had any doubt about the Jersey, the impressive account of her performances in competition with other breeds were enough finally to convince me. The two most important competitions in the dairy farming world are the Harold Jackson Trophy and the National Milk Cup. Each has, in the last twenty years, gone more often to the Jersey than to any other breed. The Jersey is the only breed to have won the Harold Jackson Trophy as many as five years in succession. The Harold Jackson Trophy is awarded to the cow of any breed gaining most points for milk and butterfat over a period of three years. The National Milk Cup is awarded to the cow of any breed yielding the most milk and butterfat in relation to body weight. It is the only National Trophy which gives a true test of efficient production, though I understand there is a trophy of similar nature shortly to be presented for international competition by that well-known cattle and poultry judge, and great champion of the Jersey cow, Mr. R. W. ('Bob') Carson. All other trophies are awarded for yield regardless of body weight, which, where cost of production is to be considered, means nothing. The real test of the breed is the efficiency of the cow as a converter of food into milk and butterfat, and in this respect, both in any costings that have been carried out and in open competition where the ratio of body weight is taken into account, the Jersey is supreme.

I am not in love with the idea of milk-production competitions, but there are times when one must stretch a point in order to establish its validity. My contention that organically bred, reared, and in particular organically fed, cattle will produce even more economically than the artificially forced animals of whatever the breed, and at the same time remain healthy is merely a statement of opinion without some practical demonstration. Consequently, in the summer of 1950 I entered two home-bred and reared 2nd calf Jerseys for the Milk and Butter Trials of the Royal Cornwall Show, and won the Seale Hayne Challenge Cup for the cow gaining most points in the Milk and Butter Tests and got 1st Prize in the Butter Tests, against 25 cows of all breeds. The same cow, Polden Dolly Daydream, also won the Reserve Supreme Championship on inspection, against all breeds. She has yielded to the time of writing, 1,200 gallons at 5.4% butterfat in 290 days with her second calf and is still giving 3 gallons daily.

CHAPTER SIXTEEN

Going Pedigree

‘**R**ear your own’ is wise advice to the man who wishes to build a pedigree attested herd. It takes a brave and skilled man to buy mature cows without buying trouble, especially if he is buying pedigree attested stock.

By far the best way of founding a pedigree herd is to buy a bunch of heifers, either in calf or bulling heifers (in my opinion the younger the better), and allow your herd to grow slowly alongside your experience. But I had a good milking non-pedigree herd when I decided to go pedigree and wished to maintain the income from that source while building the pedigree herd. So I decided on a gradual change over.

As I was aiming at attestation simultaneously with my efforts to build a pedigree herd, the first step was to have the herd tuberculin-tested. The first test showed twenty-seven reactors out of sixty-five head of stock, and all of the reactors were cows.

An interesting thing which, if not a coincidence, may be a useful guide to others, is that all the reactors were among cattle normally wintered indoors. A part of the herd was at that time housed in open-backed, exposed sheds, and not one of these cows reacted.

I decided to dispose of these twenty-seven reactors and replace them with cows in full production. With a limitation on capital, I had to purchase oldish cows which, besides being cheaper, would produce immediately a higher yield than first-calf heifers. If they had good records behind them, they would be useful for breeding young stock for the future herd.

How riddled with pitfalls is the business of buying pedigree cows. There are still breeders in all breeds who make much of the gullibility of the new breeder in the disposal of their duds. Smart as a farmer may be at the ordinary market, it takes a genius to avoid trouble when starting in a new breed.

Even in the purchase of animals that have passed all the present-day tests there is no sure safeguard. I have brought home more than one animal with a T.T. certificate, and even from an attested herd, to react badly immediately on arrival home.

The fact is that it is possible for a cow to pass the tuberculin test and yet show sufficient signs of being a subsequent reactor to enable her owner, if unscrupulous enough, to dispose of her as T.T. before she does react.

This practice of sending doubtful reactors and potential reactors to T.T. sales is bound to continue until something is done by the Government about the disposal of, and compensation for, T.T. and agglutination test reactors. Or until, failing action by the Government, farmers themselves, through their own organizations such as the National Farmers' Union or T.T. Milk Producers' Association, institute their own scheme of insurance, whereby owners of attested herds should pay a small insurance premium, the proceeds of which could be used to compensate for the isolation and treatment of reactors. It is in ways such as this that the National Farmers' Union might be better employed. A union which can help its members to be self-reliant and more efficient, and competent in their work, is a far greater asset to the nation and the world, and consequently to farmers themselves, than just another trade union concerned only to extract the highest possible prices for its members from a reluctant and disgruntled community. And the only alternative to self-organization, self-discipline and self-help is the inflicted dictatorship of a Government which may not understand our problems. If we cannot produce what the consumer wants, then compulsory regulations may force it from us in ways we don't like. Schemes such as this need only be used by the organic farmer in the costly transitional period, for in the long run it is evident that organic methods, with the supplementary use of preventive and remedial herbs, will make the need for the disposal of reactors extremely rare.

Other and perhaps greater sources of confusion in the choice of animals are the published records. I am sure more buyers are misled by records, upon which so much reliance is placed, than by any other factor. For records carelessly read, especially if they have been more carefully and deceptively produced, might mean everything or nothing at all.

In the first place, isolated yields have little or no relevance; neither have yields that bear no relationship to the age of the animal.

For instance, a heifer that produces 650 gallons with her first calf, beginning at two years old, is far more valuable than the heifer that produces 1,000 gallons with her first calf commencing the lactation at three and a half years old. Or a cow that produces a big yield after a long rest may never produce such a yield again, nor breed heifers capable of repeating her single high yield.

I had one cow that never produced more than 1,000 gallons, but after eighteen months' rest, during which time I had difficulty in getting her in calf, she did a lactation of 1,700 gallons. The important thing about that cow was not the 1,700-gallon lactation, which would be printed boldly in a sale catalogue without any reference to the rest which preceded it, but the under 1,000-gallon lactations which she did in several successive twelve-month periods.

These things I have discovered out of sad experience. But I also discovered that published information can operate in one's favour if studied with the cow's obvious potentialities observed, especially if one has some knowledge of the previous management of the cow.

I purchased one cow at a dispersal sale where I was able to gather that the management of the herd had not been as efficient as the herd deserved. The cow was stated to be giving 29 lb. a day, several weeks after calving, on the day of the sale, but I felt sure that from her appearance and udder she should do much more.

She came home to rise in yield to 56 lb. a day, and did 1,200 gallons in the lactation, although she was eight years old and had never done more than 700 gallons before.

One often reads in sale catalogues that a cow has done a certain yield in 365 days. This figure may mean that she has given the particular yield in one lactation, or that she has been got in calf again quickly and fitted one lactation and part of another into one year, thereby giving the impression from her 365-day yield that she is a better milker than a study of several lactations might reveal.

One cow in my herd completed a lactation of 980 gallons in 280 days during a recording year, but she calved again and went on to produce 1,150 gallons in the recording year of 365 days; a figure which would look much better in a catalogue but which would not deceive the buyer who studied her performance deeply.

My journey from a nondescript herd to pedigree and attestation has taught me the importance of gaining the following information about the females in the pedigrees of animals that I buy, whether cows or bulls:

1. The total yield in each recorded lactation.

2. The age of the animal at the commencement of each lactation.

3. The number of days the animal was in milk, and whether the figures refer to a continuous lactation or a recording year which may include parts of two lactations.

(All the above information is shown in the annual 'Register of Milk Records,' which reputable breeders will usually allow buyers to inspect. An inspection of this register is probably the surest guard against being misled in the matter of records.)

4. Butterfat figures for at least six or eight tests in each lactation. In view of the growing emphasis on quality, these are almost more important than milk yields. Before I changed over to Jerseys I had a Friesian cow which was a regular 1,000-galloner, but she was equally consistent with her 2.4 to 2.6 percent butterfat. If I had continued to breed from her I might have built up a very high-yielding herd, but I might also have found myself without a market for my poor-quality milk, to say nothing of the interest of the law in this matter.

5. To see the actual figures of the measurements taken at the last T.T. test and, if possible, to obtain an individual certificate with each cow. It is possible then to see whether the cow passed the test easily or whether she was a border-line case.

Don't be afraid to splash out on your bull, even if it means buying fewer females; and don't mind how long it takes to find the right one. If I were starting again I should be prepared to set aside as much for the purchase of the bull as for all the females put together, in order to get the bull I wanted.

But don't be swept off your feet by freak yields or butterfat tests in the pedigree records. I recently saw a Jersey bull sold for 1,500 guineas at an auction, because his dam had averaged butterfat tests of 6 and 7 percent in two lactations only. Her previous lactations had been normal and her ancestors showed normal butterfat tests. It is clear that such freak tests are never likely to be transmitted to the bull's progeny.

If you pay well for the bull you should be well satisfied with his potentialities. That means seeing as many of his female ancestors, and their records, as possible—certainly his dam, and go to the ends of the earth to see his grandam and sire's dam, if they are living. It will be all the more valuable if they are old, for then you will see how they wear, particularly in the udder.

Even more important are the half-sisters; and if there are any full sisters in the herd you will be a lucky man, for if the herd from which you are buying is a good established one, and the yields and butterfat tests consistent for several generations, it is almost certain that the bull will breed females as good, if not better, than his full sisters.

But when the solid foundation of a good herd is laid, on the basis of sound advice and costly experience, all the advice in the world isn't going to deprive you or me, or any other farmer worth the name, of the thrill and excitement of an occasional exercise of judgment pure and simple in the purchase of a cow.

CHAPTER SEVENTEEN

Pigs and Poultry on the Fertility Farm

In the building up of fertility, especially on the poor light-land farm, there is no animal more effective than the pig. Though I would not suggest that the pig is an *essential* part of fertility building, there is no quicker or more economical contributor to soil fertility. There is, consequently, a strong case for keeping pigs on the farm of low fertility for no other reason than that of fertility making, quite apart from any direct profits which may accrue. I kept pigs in the early days at Goosegreen and have used them in large numbers for land reclamation work which I have directed elsewhere. The system used, which has already been copied with success in a number of land reclamation schemes, was originated by my mother and brothers (M. E. Turner & Sons, Brockholes Farm, Branton, Doncaster), with their large pedigree Essex herd, before the war.

In the 1930s they took over one of the poorest blow-away sand-land farms in South Yorkshire, which was already known as incapable of growing anything without large quantities of artificial fertilizer, and because of the difficult times through which farming was passing, few farmers had the means to risk the immense cost of artificial fertilizers with no certain prospect of the resultant produce finding a profitable market. The owners of the farm were therefore unable to find a tenant for the farm, at any rent, which gives a fair guide as to the condition of the soil. My mother and brothers bravely stepped in and took on the farm, and transformed it. Losses followed for a few years while the harmful effect of heavy doses of chemicals was being experienced, but the land has now been built up to a state of fertility unequalled in the district. After the 1950 harvest (which was the worst in living memory) I had a letter from one of my brothers saying, 'We have just harvested the heaviest crops ever remembered in this district, over the whole 300 acres of the farm, without an ounce of tillage' (the North Country word for artificial fertilizers). And such results were achieved by the use of pigs, supported by the organic methods described in the rest of this book.

Tackling a field of the farm at a time, for large areas had gone back to rough grassland infested with weeds, pigs were used for every operation of reclamation, except the actual sowing of seed and levelling the ground with disc harrows.

Starting with a field in its rough state, large numbers of pigs of all ages were turned into the field and folded over it. Where there was good hedge shelter no other shelter was provided, but where the hedges were bare, rough timber and galvanized sheeting shelters were provided for sows with young litters. The Essex pigs which my brothers use seem, however, to prefer the hedge bottom to the sheds, even for farrowing.

The pigs are allowed a minimum of food, for this reason: if a large number of store pigs is available they are preferred to sows or gilts close to or just after farrowing. They then find most of their keep from the grass, weeds and roots of all kinds which they dig out as the whole field is thoroughly and completely turned over. Coarse roots of weeds, which are extremely difficult to eradicate on this rough land by any other means, are dug up by the pigs to provide food and at the same time they clean the land more effectively than is possible with a machine. Labour for attending to the pigs is reduced to the very minimum because, at the most, the pigs receive only one small feed daily, and this is raw potatoes or grain.

If the number of available pigs is limited, then folding may be resorted to, in order to ensure thorough turning of every square foot. My brothers have turned pigs on to fields as thickly as 100 to the acre in carrying out this reclamation work, but if the herd of pigs is not big enough to allow so many, the concentration may be varied by means of a fold or electric fence. If pigs of various sizes are used, two strands of electrified wire are needed, as the bigger pigs soon learn to go over the electrified single strand and the smaller pigs may go under. I have even seen a sow lying, feeding her litter, on an electrified fence which had been erected too near the ground.

When the field is completely turned over and well cultivated by the pigs, they move on to start 'ploughing' another field, and the first field is levelled and a rough seed-bed prepared with the disc harrows. Thousand-headed kale is then broadcast over the field.

When the kale has grown it provides all the food for another batch of pigs, which are again turned loose on the field or folded over sections of it. Again, if the herd is big enough to avoid the work of moving folds in order to concentrate a large number on a small area, the amount of labour needed to look after the pigs is no more than a walk around to inspect the pigs once daily. The kale is grazed by the pigs at a young leafy stage and they clear the whole crop down to the ground, leaving at the most only small stumps.

Then the disc harrows go in again, and once or twice over the field with disc harrows prepares a seed-bed ready for sowing wheat. Thick concentrations of pigs twice over the field and the consuming on the field of weeds, weed roots, and then the kale, have left a good covering of dung, lightly trodden in by the pigs and then incorporated into the topsoil by the disc harrows. On the poorest land, following this double dressing of pig manure, part of which has advanced in its decomposition, good crops of wheat have always been harvested. Even better results are obtained when fattening or breeding pigs are used to graze the kale, and are given additional feeding in the form of pig meal or cubes.

I have criticized the plough in various ways, mainly for its wastefulness of time, power and labour. But this demonstration of 'ploughs' which need neither petrol, nor oats, nor hardly any human time or labour in order to turn the turf, and which in the process of this powerless ploughing, spread fertility over the and soil—produce pork and bacon as a by-product—leaves at least one type of plough for which I have nothing but admiration.

There could be no better example of the system of farming which I have tried to advocate in this book, that is, one which takes every opportunity to observe the ways of nature, takes the fullest advantage of every free provision of nature, and simplifies every farming operation until the farm almost operates itself, with a minimum of labour.

The above system is designed primarily to take advantage of the pig as a natural land reclaimer and fertility maker, but pigs, as a business in themselves and as an income-making branch of the farm in their own right, involve rather more intensive methods, and in this case the following is my method, which differs only in a few important respects from those in general use.

Up to the time of farrowing, gilts and sows should be allowed as much fresh air and exercise as possible, and not be allowed to accumulate any excess of flesh, so that they run on in an active and healthy condition: 3 to 4 lb. of meal a day in winter, and 2 to 3 1b. a day in summer, will maintain the in-pig sows in a fit condition up to three weeks before farrowing.

15a. M.E. Turner & Son's Keresforth Grand Duchess, a typical Essex gilt reared by methods described on page 174.

15b. M. E. Turner & Son's Pedigree Essex Sow Keresforth Duchess (twice a Supreme Champion, all breeds) carrying a litter of 12, all subsequently reared.

15c. The 'fertility' plough. Reclaiming derelict land with pigs (see page 174).

16a. Soil erosion in Britain 1949. Soil blowing away in the formerly rich Fens of Lincolnshire. 'Extractive' farming, the removal of trees and hedges and repeated chemical manuring have resulted in serious soil erosion and crop pests such as eelworm. Fertility farming can prevent such scenes as this from spreading over Britain.

16b. Soil and young plants blown into dykes in the Fenlands. The first British desert may thus be caused unless it is arrested by Fertility farming.

Three weeks or a fortnight before farrowing, the sow is put into the pen, where she will remain until the farrows are weaned. The pen is well bedded with straw—chaffed straw being preferable, as the little pigs may entangle or smother themselves in long straw. The sow is given 4 or 5 lb. per day of the following ration: fish meal, meat meal or dried milk powder, 1 part; bean meal, 1 part; wheat meal, 2 parts; barley meal, 1 part; maize meal, 1 part (or barley meal, 2 parts).

As farrowing time approaches, the sow is closely watched but not interfered with, unless she is obviously in difficulties. No special feeding or treatment is necessary unless the sow is ill or weak with prolonged parturition. The sow's rations should now be increased after farrowing to 9 to 12 lb., according to the size of her litter.

The young pigs will begin to eat at three weeks of age, and they are fed separately with a mixture of dried milk powder or fish meal, 1 part; bean meal, 1 part; wheatings, 4 parts; barley meal, 2 parts; maize meal, 1 part; bran, 1 part; mixed if possible with skimmed milk.

A portion of the pen is railed off with a separate trough and made available for the young pigs but not for the sow. An ample supply of fresh green food is given daily and always, when it is available, use separated milk for mixing the meal instead of water. This is given in the proportion of 1 gallon of separated milk to each 6 lb. of meal. The main object in feeding young pigs should be to maintain, right through, the rapid liveweight gain that is made by the young pigs while sucking the sow. To do this the pigs should be given separated milk as soon as they start eating, and particularly at the time they are weaned. There is always a risk of young pigs receiving a set-back at weaning when they are taken suddenly from the sow and their rations of milk cease. As they get accustomed to being with the sow after weaning, and it is seen that they are forging ahead, then the milk may gradually be reduced.

The longer the young pigs are with the sow, and the stronger they are at weaning, the more rapid is their liveweight increase, from weaning to killing weight. Commercial pig-keeping, however, demands a limit to the length of time the young pig may stay with the sow if two litters are to be reared from each sow within the twelve months. The ideal age, then, for weaning is eight weeks.

The sow is mated again at the first heat period after weaning—usually the fourth or fifth day after the young pigs are removed. A sow put to the boar at the first heat period will always produce a bigger litter than if left until a later period. A rapid improvement in the sow's condition will take place when the young pigs leave her, and by mating at the first heat period, owing to the greater activity of the reproductive organs at this time, larger litters are obtained.

The young pigs are kept on the same ration until they are thirteen weeks old, when the mixture is gradually changed to a ration containing less protein and a higher percentage of carbohydrates. The following is an ideal mixture for the pigs from thirteen weeks onwards: dried blood or milk powder, $\frac{1}{2}$ part; palm-kernel meal, 1 part; wheat meal, 2 parts; barley meal, 5 parts; maize meal or barley meal, an additional $1\frac{1}{2}$ parts.

The fish meal is dropped in the later stages of fattening, or may be replaced all through by blood meal, dried milk powder, or some other form of high protein concentrate. This is to avoid the risk of tainting the flesh, as so often happens with a mixture containing fish meal. There are several excellent high-protein foods on the market which could quite well take the place of fish meal, and the price compares favourably with that of fish meal. Milk powder, used right through from birth, eliminates the change over from fish meal between rearing ration and fattening ration.

Given average conditions, the pig fed on these lines makes bacon 210 to 220 lb. live weight in 25 to 26 weeks.

A rough guide for the quantity of food required by growing pigs is to feed approximately $\frac{1}{4}$ lb. meal for every week of age up to 24 weeks.

The following table will summarize the meal requirements of various classes of pigs at different ages:

4 weeks old:	$\frac{1}{2}$–$\frac{3}{4}$ lb. per day, according to size of litter
8 weeks old:	$1\frac{1}{2}$–2 lb. per day
10 weeks old:	$2\frac{1}{2}$ lb. per day
12 weeks old:	3 lb. per day, gradually changing to fattening mixture
14 weeks old:	$3\frac{1}{2}$ lb. per day
16 weeks old:	4 lb. per day
20 weeks old:	5 lb. per day
24 weeks old:	6 lb. per day, which allowance should not be exceeded
Sow in pig:	3–4 lb. per day
Sow in milk:	9–12 lb. per day, according to size of litter
Working boars:	5–6 lb. per day.

It is essential that all pigs have a regular daily supply of greenstuff, if they are not running out, even if it is only a grass sod thrown into the pen. Where pigs have no access to the pasture, and a good supply of cabbage or other green food is not available, the simple

17. 'Fertility farmed' crops showing weedless stubble on land cropped without ploughing for three years. (See pages 25-26).

18a. Just dropped! The field is the best place for a cow to calve.

18b. Some of the author's herd including three 15-year-old cows. In the centre foreground, a prize-winning home-reared heifer yielding 54 lb. milky daily with her first calf, on home-grown food.

most needed. The earthworms will continue to breed under the litter, providing a continuous 'self-service canteen.'

Litter in the form of straw is added to this base periodically as the hens break it down by means of scratching and pecking. Daily, or as often as may seem advisable, the litter and compost is forked over and into rough heaps, exposing the bottom of the yard and bringing to the surface more food for the fowls. They will scratch it back as they find their food and break up the fresh litter and mix it with the partially decayed material.

Litter is also provided in the shed, where the birds operate in wet weather. Food and water is provided in the usual way, in the house, but far less than the usual protein ration is needed where earthworms are added and encouraged.

A corner of the yard is covered with galvanized sheeting to provide a dust bath.

PART 5

Animal Diseases
Their Prevention and Treatment by Natural
Methods, and with the Aid of Herbs

.

CHAPTER EIGHTEEN

Livestock Diseases

The foregoing details of soil management and cropping are basic to the whole livestock economy of the farm. For without it there was nothing but continuous disease in the herd, and it is only as this system of soil management and cropping has been developed that the complete programme of disease prevention and treatment has been possible.

Some account of my cattle disease experience may therefore now follow in more detail.

It is always difficult for a farmer to assess the cost of disease in his herd, and few farmers would give any estimate of this cost which is a charge on the income of every orthodox farm. Partly because it is not good business for a farmer to admit that disease reduces in any considerable degree his annual profits, for nobody wants to buy cattle from a diseased herd, and partly because the drain of disease can only be estimated, few farmers care to go to this trouble of reminding themselves of a misfortune which they accept as inevitable and largely unavoidable.

But I could not accept disease as inevitable and I determined to eradicate it. I was naturally interested to know what it was costing me, and therefore kept some records, from which I quote for the losses in the year 1942–3, directly attributable to disease, which in my subsequent experience I now know to be avoidable where organic methods of farming—and livestock management in particular—are practised.

The figures relate specifically to 'contagious' abortion.

Loss of milk, due to the cow aborting while dry, or nearly dry, and losing a complete lactation. The loss is estimated on the actual recorded yield of the cow's previous lactation, though in most cases it may be assumed that, given normal health, the cow would have given an increased yield in the year in question.

Cowslip	800 gallons	Strawberry	800 gallons
Snowdrop	500 ,,	Poppy	300 ,,
Cherry	800 ,,	Charity	500 ,,
Melody	700 ,,	Red May (twice)	600 ,,
Collette	800 ,,	Silver Star	300 ,,
Baroness	800 ,,	Curly	100 ,,
	200 ,,	Sonda	300 ,,
Dream	400 ,,		
Beauty	800 ,,		
		Total	8,700 gallons

At the average price of 2/– (£.10) a gallon, £870

Loss on cows sold barren or unsound as a result of abortion, see opposite page.

The losses which can therefore be directly traced to the contagious abortion are as follows:

	£	s.	d.	2006* £	$
Milk	870	0	0	28,040	51,594
Cattle	374	10	0	12,054	22,227
Cost of Vaccinations	30	0	0	967	1,779
	£1,274	10	0	£41,061	$75,600

Editor's note: The author's historic financial data was converted to modern currencies and approximately adjusted for inflation, using the consumer price index. This most certainly will not correlate to modern costs and prices, but should be utilized for general directional trends only.

This does not take any account of the immense losses from dead calves, seventeen of which were recorded in that year, as it is difficult to make an estimate of the value which these calves would have had alive. The calves from the pedigree cattle, whether bulls or heifers, would have had a good value. Nor have I included the cost of numerous orthodox veterinary treatments of cows for sterility and other attendant troubles after abortion, most of which treatments were a failure. Nor what is probably the greatest loss of all, the interference with breeding policy and plans for a level output of milk. Everything, in the way of farm planning, goes by the board when contagious abortion takes charge, resulting in untold losses which cannot be directly estimated.

LIVESTOCK DISEASES

Name of Cow	December 1941 Value			Selling Price 1942–3			Gain			Loss		
	£	s.	d.	£	s.	d.	£	s.	d.	£	s.	d.
Ladybird	60	0	0	48	0	0	—			20	0	0
Spark	30	0	0	20	0	0	—			10	0	0
Spider	38	0	0	16	0	0	—			22	0	0
Favourite	35	0	0	40	0	0	5	0	0	—		
Pretty	40	0	0	30	5	0	—			9	15	0
Snowdrop	60	0	0	6	10	0	—			53	10	0
Lotty	35	0	0	25	0	0	—			10	0	0
Dairymaid	65	0	0	20	5	0	—			44	15	0
Smuttynose	34	0	0	30	0	0	—			4	0	0
Duchess	25	0	0	20	0	0	—			5	0	0
Cherry	30	0	0	16	0	0	—			14	0	0
Priscella	48	0	0	30	0	0	—			18	0	0
Blue	35	0	0	18	0	0	—			17	0	0
Bobtail	25	0	0	20	0	0	—			5	0	0
Mona	25	0	0	16	0	0	—			9	0	0
Picture	30	0	0	19	0	0	—			11	0	0
Lady	25	0	0	14	0	0	—			11	0	0
Lily	35	0	0	25	0	0	—			10	0	0
Lofty	50	0	0	32	0	0	—			18	0	0
Ruby	32	0	0	30	0	0	—			2	0	0
Binkles	25	0	0	6	0	0	—			19	0	0
Greta	18	0	0	25	0	0	7	0	0	—		
Lovely	45	0	0	40	0	0	—			5	0	0
Daisey	35	0	0	20	0	0	—			15	0	0
Sarah	25	0	0	25	0	0	—			—		
Mousey	10	0	0	2	0	0	—			8	0	0
Irish	25	0	0	20	0	0	—			5	0	0
Fatty	25	0	0	15	0	0	—			10	0	0
Brenda	30	0	0	25	0	0	—			5	0	0
Dolly	15	0	0	14	0	0	—			1	0	0
Baby	40	0	0	49	10	0	9	10	0	—		
Brin	45	0	0	20	0	0	—			25	0	0
Molly	30	0	0	22	0	0	—			8	0	0
			Total				21	10	0	395	0	0
					Less Gain					21	10	0
					Net Loss				£374	10	0

Total	692.96	12,731.06		Total	1,275.05	23,425.15
Less Gain	692.96			Less Gain	1,275.05	
Net Loss	£12,054.22			Net Loss	$22,179.76	

193

CHAPTER NINETEEN

Tackling Disease

All the help that the orthodox veterinary profession has been able to offer me in connection with animal diseases, failed hopelessly to get me out of my difficulties. I think the outstanding reason for this is that all orthodox treatment is based on the assumption that disease is *caused* by bacteria; that disease is contracted solely by infection, and that the injection of a culture of the disease bacteria, or of a substance calculated to kill the 'offending' bacteria, will enable the animal to resist the disease. In my experience, these assumptions have been shown to be wildly wide of the mark.

Bacteria which are found to be active in diseased animals are *secondary* to the unhealthy condition in the animal body, and not themselves the cause. Indeed, I would go so far as to say that the bacteria arise *as a result* of the condition, though this is not to deny the fact of a disease developing through contact, provided the necessary conditions for the development of the disease are first present in the animal 'contracting' the disease. The fact is that a cow in sound health does not succumb to disease, and it was in this fact—that many of my animals remained untouched by the flood of active bacteria which surrounded them—that I found the clue to my solution of all cattle disease problems. Having convinced myself that bacteria do not multiply in the healthy body, I was able to exonerate bacteria as the primary cause of disease. Having dismissed bacteria as the culprit and indeed concluded that nature probably had a good purpose for the bacteria which are found in the diseased condition, the solution of the problem of disease became a simple process of elimination.

I asked myself what were the main changes in our management of cattle since the days when disease was rare; what were the main differences, that our herds should contain so much more disease today than they did in my father's and grandfather's day? And the answer came back like a shot: intensified exploitation of the dairy cow, artificial feeding, and the mad race for higher and higher yields, with all the attendant artificial practices which have multiplied as disease has become more widespread. Vaccination has increased in proportion to the incidence of disease, which at once brings it under suspicion as one of the *causes* of disease—if we operate this system of deduction—rather than the preventive which we have blindly believed it to be.

I could only get at the true cause of disease by eliminating these factors which have grown in the same ratio as the incidence of disease. By process of elimination I was able to find the factors which had made the greatest contribution to the development and increase of disease. To have allowed these causes to remain, and attempt disease eradication by treating the symptoms, in the way that the veterinary practitioner was doing, would only have landed me in the bankruptcy court and my cows deeper in the swamp of disease which threatened to engulf them.

I came to the conclusion that abortion, mastitis, sterility and tuberculosis, as well as most other diseases of cattle, had their real foundation in the toxic condition of the animal body, brought about by unnatural methods of management. The fact that these diseases are rare among young stock (it is generally only when the animal has undergone at least one lactation that the real trouble starts, though of course heredity is gaining in its power of predisposition to disease and bringing our young stock more immediately under the burden of disease), and less common in the beef breeds, indicated that it was management for milk production rather than bacterial infection which was the primary cause.

Thus I reached my conclusions regarding the real causes of disease in cattle, which I summarize as follows:

(1) Artificial feeding with concentrated foods which lack the health factors of fresh whole foods, or home-grown foods which are forced with chemical fertilizers to grow faster than the capacity of the plant to absorb the natural health agents of the soil. Scientific feeding of dairy cattle has as its primary aim the stimulation of maximum milk yield with little consideration for the health of the cow, and no means of assuring the provision of those health essentials which are contained in fresh food grown in naturally manured, humus-rich soil, and which the nutritionist has so far failed to isolate and prepare artificially for inclusion in manufactured compound foods. Plant hormones, for instance, are no doubt a potent factor in the development of hormone secretions in the animal body, for we now know the imperative necessity of an adequate hormone supply in the body. Yet hormones cannot be

substituted artificially through the plant to the animal in the way that nature provides. Under modern methods of management the higher the yield of the cow the less natural food is she allowed to have; hence the greater her potentiality for milk production the lower her intake of the foods which are rich in natural health factors. Health goes in at the mouth, and if we cut down the health-giving foods provided by nature to function in ways we cannot fully understand, all the veterinary surgeons in the world will not save our cows from the doom which commercial 'science' is designing for them.

(2) The cow is expected to produce a heavy milk yield, and at the same time to build the foetus of the calf in her womb. Under natural conditions the cow does not become pregnant again until she has completed the task of rearing one calf and has ceased to produce milk, or at least has declined in her output to the extent that milk production in no way draws from the necessary nutriment of the foetus. Nature asks of the cow only *one* thing at a time, and she does this efficiently with no risk of disease. (If cattle diseases had been multiplying as rapidly before man's domestication of the cow, as they have done in the last century, she would have long ago become an extinct species.) Man asks of the cow at least *two* things at a time, and though the cow may just succeed in doing them both she does so at grave peril to her health. Not only does man ask so much more than nature, but he tries to force the process to the utmost of the cow's capacity, and indeed beyond.

(3) Further, taking away the calf at birth—and now, with artificial insemination even disallowing the natural contact with the bull— deprives the cow of emotional factors which bring direct stimulus to milk production and breeding ability. At the time of writing a third of all cattle served in this country are artificially inseminated, and there is nothing to indicate in the sales catalogues of pedigree sales whether or not the animal offered for sale is the result of a natural service or a veterinary surgeon's test-tube injection. Not only will the removal of the calf at birth deprive the cow of the essential stimulus of suckling, which encourages the secretions of the uterus and udder, and the cleansing of both after calving, but the calf when mature is bound to suffer from this deprivation of its natural food and the substitution of calf gruel which cannot provide *all* that nature intended.

It is not surprising, then, that sooner or later there is a breakdown of the cow's constitution, at the point of greatest strain, usually the udder or the uterus. It is at this stage that I believe nature takes the opportunity to rid the body of the toxins which have accumulated from unnatural feeding. This is done by a discharge of catarrhal mucous by way of the walls of the uterus, resulting in the inability of the foetus to remain embedded in the uterus—abortion—or by way of the udder—mastitis. Bacteria already present in the body, awaiting their task of cleansing the body and assisting the consumption of toxic accumulations, develop and consume the wastes of the body. If the body continues to be fed with the food which has given rise to those toxic accumulations, the bacteria multiply beyond all bounds—run amok, so to speak—and consume, in addition to their rightful toxins, the tissues of the body. If we fast the animal, and supply known and harmless natural purifiers such as garlic, the bacteria perform the task of cleansing, the body continues to eliminate by means of the catarrhal discharges which, during a fast, are evident from all excretory passages of the body, and the condition may be completely remedied.

If, however, the bacteria are killed, as they are by orthodox treatment, the toxic accumulations remain unconsumed, and though some will be eliminated by the uterus or udder discharges, much will remain to give rise to future attempts on the part of nature to consume or discharge what is foreign to the system, and 'disease' in one form or another will recur.

All this meant for me the following new approach to disease. I became convinced that any attempt to reduce disease by the usual practices of vaccination and germ killing were certain to fail, unless all the factors contributing to a breakdown of the natural forces were eliminated.

I could not hope to reduce disease unless I decided to co-operate with nature. This meant that if I wanted higher yields I must get them by breeding rather than feeding; that I must ask of the cow only what she would comfortably produce on organically grown food without forcing, and that any increased yields in my herd should be obtained from the bull by a process of upgrading.

It meant that I must allow my cows the fullest opportunity for the exercise of natural stimuli—the suckling calf and the natural sex relationship. It meant that I would allow my cows and bulls the freedom of natural life, as far as was possible, instead of tying them by the neck for several months of the year.

Above all, it meant that my cows must be given their food, as far as possible, while it still had its roots in Mother Earth. And, in the degree to which such natural feeding was not possible, I must provide the widest possible variety of herbs as sources of the mineral and trace elements essential to health.

I must provide adequately of all the bulky natural foods before considering concentrated feeding; kale, silage, hay and straw must come before cake.

I am confident that if we, as farmers, made ourselves more conversant with nature's ways of preventing disease, and imitated them, as far as possible, instead of ignoring them or even opposing them (as it has so blatantly been the practice of 'science' in our generation), then we could say good-bye for ever to the hypodermic needle and the manufacturing chemist.

I hope most profoundly that the immense vested interests in disease will not be so powerful as to prevent this natural course of events, for I believe most earnestly that the future of not only the bovine, but the human race, depend upon it.

My previous chapters on soil management, cropping, and herbal leys, provide the basis of disease prevention and the essentials of health maintenance. In subsequent chapters I shall describe my approach to specific diseases, with some account of my natural methods of treatment of the diseases with which my herd was infested and which, indeed, are the scourge of most dairy farmers of the world. I am grateful to the many breeders who have provided me with 'incurable' animals with which to work out my treatments. None of them suffered, for natural treatment does not call for the horrors of vivisection, and all except one or two that were anatomically defective were cured by methods set out in the succeeding pages of this book.

CHAPTER TWENTY

Mastitis

There was a time when I followed all the correct routines in the anti-germ warfare. My cows, my staff, my milking parlour and milking machine were almost continually submerged in disinfectant! I should have thought it impossible for the most evasive germ to penetrate the armoury of my germicidal front. But cows continued to go wrong in the udder with monotonous regularity. I might as well have saved my time. I decided I *would* save my time and stopped all the complicated procedure of germ warfare, incidentally saving myself a considerable sum of money formerly spent on disinfectants. The germ now had a free hand. My herd was completely defenceless. Maybe the germs took pity on a defenceless enemy, for though I might have expected now to find mastitis rampant in every udder in the herd, the disease went quietly on as before, just as though the disinfectants had never been there at all!

I concluded that both the experts and I had been chasing an illusion, and decided to experiment on a different line altogether. After the experimenting with the application of the virulent discharges from an infected quarter to the udder of a healthy cow without result, I changed my attitude to the germs completely.

I made notes of every little thing that touched upon each case of mastitis: heat periods; milk yield; stage of pregnancy; period of attack before or after heat period; or, if after service, length of time after service; type and quantity of ration that the cow had been on; treatment used, with result and subsequent state of the quarter in the next lactation; whether the cow had been milked on a machine unit that had recently milked an infected cow; type of discharge; length of time the cow had suckled her calf before coming into the milking herd; whether the cow had been difficult to get in calf at the last service, and all factors likely to have a bearing on the cause of the trouble.

My experimental failure to spread the disease by contact was clearly confirmed by subsequent events. This does not mean to say that the existence of bacteria in mastitis-infected udders was discounted altogether. But I did become convinced that it was wrong to approach the trouble with the object of killing the bacteria. For they have a benevolent purpose in the udder. If they are killed and the udder appears to be cured (which in any case is a rare thing where germicidal treatment is employed), as likely as not the udder goes wrong at a later date in the very same place. But where a cure is achieved without the use of germicidal measures it is permanent.

The second remarkable fact was that there is an undeniable relationship between the critical stages of a cow's sexual life and the incidence of mastitis. Practically every case that I have studied has occurred at a time which coincides with a particular phase of the sexual cycle. With empty cows at the time of the heat period, and with pregnant cows, it can usually be calculated to coincide with what would have been a heat period had the cow not been pregnant. My herd was suffering from abortion during the time I studied mastitis, and I found that the commonest time for mastitis trouble in the udder of a pregnant cow was also the time at which a cow commonly aborts; that is at the third, fifth or seventh months of pregnancy. And a cow often showed signs of aborting and went wrong in the udder at the same time. If I succeeded in curing the udder trouble the cow would recover from her threatened abortion, indicating a strain on the whole delicate and closely linked mechanism of milk production and reproduction.

Thirdly, a cow that is more difficult to get in calf is also more likely to succumb to mastitis. A frequent occurrence is for a cow which has been difficult to get in calf to go wrong in a quarter about three weeks after an effective service, indicating that the strain of fertilization has had an effect on the udder and the success of fertilization has been at the expense of the udder—the animal's system being unequal to effective milk production and pregnancy at the same time.

Fourthly, the disease is much more common among high-yielding cows that are receiving a large ration of concentrated food. And in the moderate milking cows, if they get trouble at all, it is more often during the time when winter feeding is in progress and not so much when the animal is receiving no food except the grass. Summer mastitis is an exception to this rule. Like a summer cold in humans, it is a natural cleansing process stimulated by the beneficial effects of sun and the more natural diet of the summer months. The toxic accumulations of winter are thus eliminated, generally by heifers or animals that have not necessarily been fed on concentrates, to an extent that would cause trouble in the winter. These attacks are usually mild if caught and treated at once.

The bacteria most frequently found in cases of mastitis are various staphylococci and streptococci which are also the bacteria said to be the cause of boils in human beings. But we all know that boils are caused not by bacteria but by excessive or indiscreet diet. The fact that staphylococcus pyogenes, for instance, is found in the pus of a boil is secondary to the real cause, which is systemic. Wrong diet causes an accumulation of poisonous matter in one part of the body or another, and nature takes the first opportunity of discharging it at the weakest point. In the meantime, bacteria multiply in the process of consuming the matter which is alien to the body, and while there is more waste to discharge, the bacteria continue to multiply. A man who will fast on the appearance of a boil discovers that the discharge soon ceases. The waste is eliminated by the many processes of nature, of which consumption by bacteria is one. Mastitis, which is in the same category as the human boil, may be approached in the same way, bringing us to the following conclusions.

Mastitis is a catarrhal discharge thrown off by the cow's system at the point of greatest strain, and is the result of systemic toxaemia brought on by one of two factors, either a diet which is not equal in its content of the natural vitamins and plant hormones (which are the prerequisites of the natural cleansing processes of healthy gland secretions) to the output demands upon the cow. So the process breaks down. Toxic catarrh replaces the natural hormone secretions of the mucous membrane of the udder. Or, an excess of unnatural feeding causes the accumulation of toxic matter in various parts of the body which must be discharged in various ways, by mastitis, big knee, influenza or pneumonia, leucorrhea (whites), or abortion, all of which result in a catarrhal discharge, when the opportunity occurs, from one or other part of the body.

In either case, if the excessive or inadequate feeding is continued, the trouble becomes chronic. But if the fault is corrected, first by a period of fasting, with frequent stripping and other efforts to eliminate mucus until the discharge ceases, followed by a completely natural diet devoid of artificial foods and composed primarily of green foods, roots, hay, straw and silage, the trouble will clear itself—and in the process the cow will become healthier in every other respect. She may not give quite so much milk in that lactation, but at least she will have many more healthy lactations, and any progeny she may bear will be one step nearer perfect health than she was herself.

Mechanical injury is of course another matter, which cannot be expected to respond to natural treatment quite so quickly as mastitis caused by systemic toxaemia. Mastitis resulting from mechanical injury is usually the aftermath of bad machine milking or a blow from another cow. This is how the milking machine is wrongly blamed for udder trouble. In my experience, a milking machine cannot cause, or spread, udder trouble when properly used.

The fallacy that the machine spreads the disease may be discounted in the properly managed herd, for, as I have previously stated, a healthy udder will not contract mastitis even when in contact with virulent bacteria. The bacteria cannot develop in the udder unless there is a catarrhal discharge to be consumed.

But trouble does often result from rough usage of the udder by a careless machine milker, and the man who blames his milking machine *or* bacteria for mastitis, is merely admitting that he is a bad farmer.

Treatment for Mastitis

On the first sign of abnormality in the milk or udder I stop all food and allow water only until the milk becomes normal. A strong dose of garlic is given in some form and repeated morning and night for a week or more: two whole garlic plants, chopped up and made into a ball with a little molasses and bran, or four tablets of garlic fortified with the herb fenugreek (see Appendix for suppliers). I milk out the affected quarter as often as possible—at least four times daily, but hourly if possible, or allow a calf to suckle it, making sure that it draws off the affected quarter.

If there is any sign of inflammation in the udder apply alternate hot and cold fomentations, with massage, three times daily, to the affected quarter, or quarters, until the inflammation goes, and during treatment finish off with a cold-water hose turned on to the udder and over the loins, for ten minutes, thoroughly soaking the region of the pelvis and udder. This stimulates a quick exchange of blood and speeds natural purification.

Work in the assumption that the mastitis is a catarrhal discharge resulting either from over-feeding or feeding on a diet which is deficient in the vitamins and plant hormones essential to milk production. Fast the animal to give the body an opportunity to eliminate this catarrhal discharge naturally and assist this elimination by milking out the discharge as often as possible.

Continue the fast for as long as three days—after which, if the milk is still not normal, a quart of cane molasses may be given, diluted in warm water, as a drench—divided into three doses daily for a further two days, but still without food. Continue the purifying garlic morning and night.

If the mastitis is caught soon enough, such a long fast should not be necessary. Twenty-four hours is generally long enough if the animal has no food whatsoever. But if the fast needs to be continued for more than twenty-four hours, then a daily rectal enema will be necessary to clear toxins from the intestines.

When discharge has ceased we resume feeding with green food only—green food grown on composted land without any chemical manures. We continue for a further week entirely on green food, without any concentrated food.

The orthodox treatment is to *suppress* the discharge by means of penicillin or sulphonilamide, but unless the catarrh which causes the trouble is *eliminated* it will recur.

In addition to the feeding of natural food rich in herbs, providing the necessary minerals and plant hormones, a weekly dose of garlic—four whole plants or six tablets—and a daily dessertspoonful of seaweed powder, are excellent preventive measures.

The udder and reproductive organs are, more than any other organ in the body, dependent on efficient glandular secretions, particularly in a cow which inherits the capacity for high milk yields, and unless the diet is rich in the natural prerequisites of these secretions udder, or breeding trouble is inevitable.

CHAPTER TWENTY-ONE

Other Diseases

Other diseases and the natural treatment I have found to be completely effective, except where mechanical or structural defect has made a cure impossible:

STERILITY

To commence the treatment, the affected animal is confined without food of any kind for a period of at least seven days—for the first and second days it is also deprived of water. If it appears to be in good condition at the end of seven days the fast is extended for a further week, allowing a limited amount of water, i.e. about one bucketful morning and night. Warm-water rectal and vaginal enemas are given once daily during the fast, using at least four gallons of water each time for each enema, rectal and vaginal. It is preferable to continue the enema each time until the water discharged is clear. The last half-gallon of water of each enema contains four crushed garlic tablets, which are retained in the intestines and uterus respectively, if possible, as long as the cow will naturally hold the water.

A dose of garlic, the whole of two chopped or flaked garlic plants twice daily, or four tablets of prepared garlic morning and night, are given during the fast. To this is added a drench of the liquid from a bucketful of fresh raspberry leaves, or two to three ounces of dried raspberry leaves soaked, or boiled, in hot water. The garlic helps to eliminate the toxins which cause sterility, and the raspberry-leaf tea has a powerful tonic effect on the uterus and organs of reproduction.

When the fast is ended the animal is reintroduced to compost grown green food only, such as oats and vetches, kale, or any other composted green crop available, or failing this to controlled grazing of pasture which has received a dressing of compost during the last two years.

A small field with not too much growth is suitable for this, and if the growth is not too lush the cow can be turned on to it continuously.

The animal is continued on compost-grown green food only for a period of five weeks, then reintroduced to compost-grown cereals. Linseed—mixed in the proportions of one part linseed to two parts coarsely ground compost-grown wheat (the richest source of vitamin E—the anti-sterility vitamin)—is given, in addition to the green food, up to a maximum of 3 lb. per animal, morning and night. After a few days of this diet the animal is returned gradually to a production ration of 4 lb. per gallon of milk produced. The production ration consists of one part ground linseed to three parts ground oats, with the addition of a little coarsely ground wheat. One dessertspoonful of seaweed powder daily provides the best natural mineral supplement.

TUBERCULOSIS

I will not elaborate on this disease at this time, for I am still engaged on experiments in its treatment. The obvious course, in relation to tuberculosis, is to see that it does not arise, by following the health maintenance methods which arc inherent in fertility farming.

But I can say at this stage that in nearly all cases of animals reacting to the tuberculin test, which often merely means that the blood-stream of the animal is in a toxic condition and not that she is tubercular, the immediate adoption of the treatment set out above for Sterility (omitting the raspberry-leaf tea) has proved effective and the animal has subsequently passed the test.

My present senior stock bull is a typical example of the many tuberculin-test reactors which have been reclaimed by this treatment. Longmoor Mogulla's Top Sergente by name, he is a most valuable pedigree Jersey whose dam won the Harold Jackson Trophy for milk and butterfat, against all breeds, and whose grandsire won supreme championships at all the main shows both in England and in Jersey. His reaction to the tuberculin test was so violent that the Ministry would not allow a retest and insisted on the disposal of the animal. But I could not afford to lose him and after moving him to some off-land I gave him this natural treatment and restored the deficiencies which gave rise to his toxaemia by a careful diet of fresh food grown from virile soil. He was tested three times in the space of a year and showed a gradual improvement until at last he was clear. The Ministry of Agriculture veterinary surgeon then gave him two clear tests at two-monthly intervals and re-admitted him to the herd, free from disease, in which condition he has continued to do his work for the past five years, showing no further sign of reaction. He is now ten years old and still working and winning prizes.

All my work indicates that tuberculosis can permanently be prevented and cured on food grown in properly managed soil, provided an adequate diet of mineral-rich herbs is given.

RHEUMATISM

Cattle quickly lose flesh while limping about with rheumatism. It is useless to attempt to put on flesh by good feeding until the toxic matter which is causing the rheumatism has been eliminated. To feed an animal that is lame with rheumatism will only exaggerate her disability.

Similarly, external massage alone, particularly with a counter-irritant, is useless. The playing of cold water on to the affected part for ten minutes morning and night, during the treatment outlined below, will, however, help to speed the cure by stimulating the blood circulation at the point of toxic accumulation, thereby assisting the process of purification.

All food is withheld from the animal, and a fast continued for a week or until the lameness has disappeared—whichever is the shorter. During the fast nothing whatever is given except water, and the animal is confined in a house without straw bedding. Rectal enemas are given daily during the fast, using a bucketful of warm water each time. Garlic is given morning and night at the rate of four tablets or two whole plants.

At the end of the fast the animal is introduced gradually to compost-grown green food only for a week, unless the lameness appears by that time to be quite cured, in which case a little hay is also introduced.

Thereafter, we gradually bring the cow back on to her normal diet, having regard to the fact that the feeding of manufactured concentrates is to be particularly avoided. The best production ration is made up of three parts (by weight) ground oats to one part linseed. All cereals, as with green food, are organically grown, and it is advisable always, when feeding sick animals, to choose foods grown on soil which has received good dressings of properly made compost.

Should the condition not be completely cured by one treatment, or, in the event of it recurring at a later date, this treatment is repeated periodically until the animal is completely healthy, ensuring in the intervals between treatments that the animal has an adequate supply of organically grown bulky food. Grazing, which includes a wide variety of herbs and the regular use of garlic in some form, is essential if there is any tendency to rheumatism.

CALF SCOUR

The immediate treatment, on the first sign of scour of any kind, is cessation of all food.

Where white scour appears in calves it is generally a result of wrong feeding, usually too high a proportion of protein in the food, or too much milk. Bacteria are quite secondary and are again nature's means of dealing with dietary abnormality.

The calf is fasted for twenty-four hours on cold water only, and if the scour then appears to have diminished the calf is re-introduced to fresh whole milk diluted with equal parts of warm water. If the calf is sucking a cow it is reintroduced to small feeds of not more than three minutes' duration four times a day, making certain the calf does not receive more than a maximum of six pints of milk during the day. Generally, with a calf that is sucking a cow, a half-gallon is sufficient, though with bucket feeding one gallon a day should be given when the calf is once more in normal health.

If the scour is still bad after a twenty-four-hour fast, the fast is continued a further day, allowing cold water only. If the scour then still persists, gentle warm-water enemas of four to eight pints twice daily are applied, reintroducing the calf to diluted milk after a maximum of two days' fasting which, with enemas, is sufficient to eliminate the scour completely.

JOHNE'S DISEASE

My experience of Johne's Disease started when I was a boy on my father's farm in Yorkshire, between twenty and thirty years ago. It was the first disease of dairy cows of any significance to us and certainly the first in my experience—and before I farmed on my own I had lived with and studied scores of Johne's Disease cases, both alive and dead. Apart from occasional difficult calvings, we had no troubles with our cattle at all. We had certainly never had any trouble which resulted in the death of the cow, as it did inevitably with every Johne's-diseased cow. We had heard of animals dying of tuberculosis, but even T.B. losses had not touched us and were apparent only on farms where cattle were seriously underfed. My father had always fed his cattle well—as everything else on the farm, including his own family, though we were never allowed to eat until every animal on the farm had been given a meal.

My most vivid impression of this disease, as long ago as those boyhood days, was my disillusionment regarding the veterinary profession. I had till then regarded the veterinary surgeon as something of a wonder man capable almost of miracles with animals. Yet here seemed to be the simple fact of diarrhoea against which the whole veterinary profession was helpless. It seemed hard to me that this onset of diarrhoea should, in spite of anything the vet could do, always result in the slow wasting away to death for every cow that got it. I thought it hard that this attack of diarrhoea should mean certain death for the cow, whereas if I had diarrhoea it was merely a sign that my diet had been somewhat indiscreet and I'd better go easy at the table for a while.

And here, of course, was my clue. For at that time manufactured cattle cakes were becoming increasingly popular and we were using a lot more than the cow's stomach was designed to digest. It is generally accepted that diarrhoea in human beings is a dietary matter, resulting in fermentation in some part of the alimentary canal. May not the same be true of cattle, I thought. And around this thought I have studied the subject of Johne's Disease ever since.

The widespread incidence of Johne's Disease coincided with the general use of manufactured cattle foods and the consequent deteriorating digestion of the animal. Far from being caused by a mysterious virus, which is the usual explanation of a trouble for which there is no obvious cause, and for which there is no orthodox cure, Johne's Disease starts with incompletely digested food remaining in the intestines and setting up fermentation which, if not eliminated quickly, breaks down the mucous membrane of the intestines, and eventually even the walls themselves. The corrugations which form on the walls of the intestine are an attempt on the part of the system naturally to localize the toxic wastes. Incomplete digestion causes in the early stages an excessive appetite, but the continued intake of food to be added to the fermenting wastes already present merely aggravates the condition, and as the fermentation develops, and inflammation of the mucous membrane sets in, loss of appetite follows and wasting begins.

The simple prevention of Johne's Disease is a diet of natural foods, and if there is no alternative to the limited feeding of concentrated prepared foods, then occasional fasting is necessary to enable the system to eliminate the residues of unnatural food which are never completely digested or absorbed by the body.

19. The perfect winter food for all cattle. Silage from pits on Plates 11a and 14b. Goosegreen Jerseys live almost entirely on this and summer grazing. Young stock live on silage and hay or oat straw from weaning age.

20a. Bull in advanced state of Johne's disease. All the author's cattle had frequent contact during this bull's stay of three months at Goosegreen Farm. No case of Johne's disease has followed during four years since.

20b. Longmoor Mogullas Top Sergente. At 4 years old rejected by Ministry of Agriculture on account of T.B. Treated for nine months by Newman Turner and returned to herd. Now 10 years old and has never shown a sign of reaction or other ill-health since he returned to the herd. He has never been without a prize at many shows in all parts of the south-west, even in his ninth year.

It is essential that the diet should contain a high proportion of fresh organically grown foods rich in vitamins, trace elements, and plant hormones, all of which are essential to complete digestion. It is probably the absence of these pre-requisites of good digestion from the food ingested, rather than the concentrated nature of the manufactured food itself, which is the real cause of the trouble. For it is not until the animal has had many months of unnatural food that she starts to scour—the first sign that the digestion is impaired. The feeding of food which does not supply the vital elements necessary to healthy digestion and assimilation—and which in any case is difficult to digest by the bovine stomach designed for bulky foods—has a cumulative effect which the animal system eventually fails to cope with; and the cow herself at last refuses food; then, however, it is too late.

PREVENTION

A herd which is naturally reared from birth—*with calves suckled on cows an essential*, for nothing impairs the digestion more effectively than gruels and calf cakes at an early age, though it may not become apparent until cowhood—which is fed on organically grown bulky food, with a high proportion of fresh grass or its nearest winter equivalent, silage, tripodded hay, and kale, supplemented where necessary with herbs and organic minerals such as seaweed in some form, will never suffer from Johne's Disease. But even in a herd so managed any animal showing the first sign of digestive trouble, with scouring, should be fasted at once for at least twenty-four hours or until normal again. This will eliminate any possibility of an accumulation of the causes of intestinal fermentation or inflammation.

TREATMENT

If for any reason Johne's Disease has developed—provided the mucous membrane of the intestine is still sound and there is no sign of blood in the dung—it is possible to save the animal by keeping the whole alimentary tract free from food until it is quite clear of fermenting wastes. This may mean fasting the animal for one or two weeks, in which case daily enemas should be given with the dosage of garlic advised for sterility. After a week of complete fasting the animal may be given a gruel of powdered fenugreek seed, with the addition of powdered tree barks available from veterinary herbal firms.

A two-pint gruel may be prepared by using a dessertspoonful of fenu-greek powder[1] and a dessertspoonful of tree barks blend[1] stirred into a smooth paste, with an equal quantity of cane molasses, then diluted with warm water or milk. Give one pint morning and night.

This will form a soothing jelly-like gruel which will act as an internal poultice and assist the healing of the alimentary tract, and at the same time provide an easily digested nutritive food.

The animal will live for weeks on this gruel, but after a week some solid green food may be tried if the dung appears to be of normal consistency. If the dung from this solid food continues to be passed in normal condition, the animal may be assumed to be cured and the quantity of green food then gradually increased to normal. If diarrhoea again results, then the fast on gruel should be continued for a further week— and so on, until the animal is found to be able to deal with solid food.

The garlic should be continued daily indefinitely, as an assistance to the elimination of mucus and the general purification of the blood-stream.

If animals are being properly fed and managed, there need be no fear of the infection of others. This I have demonstrated with my own cattle. When I addressed a large agricultural discussion group, at Bures in Suffolk, some years ago, an old Jersey breeder had the time of his life, in the front row, trying to tie me in knots, and challenged me to prove the effectiveness of my methods in disease prevention and resistance by allowing my cattle to have contact with a case of Johne's Disease. He was prepared to accept my claims for other diseases—but could not believe that this dreaded mystery disease could be resisted even by the healthiest of animals.

I answered that if anyone could produce an advanced case of Johnes I would take it on to my farm. No one accepted the challenge, but I eventually found a bull which proved to be suffering from Johne's Disease and, as the photograph shows, he was in an advanced condition and eventually died on the farm. Every animal on the farm had frequent contact with him. This was four years ago—and I have had no evidence of any trouble, certainly not Johne's Disease, which could be attributed to the bull.

BLOWN OR BLOAT OR HOVEN

The condition known as Blown, which is the subject of so much conjecture in the orthodox veterinary profession, is another of the problems which fertility farming has solved.

---

[1] From herbal firms. See Appendix.

Blown, which is also known as bloat or hoven, is the condition in which gases collect in the first stomach of the cow, and if not stopped may cause distension of the stomach to the extent of asphyxiation and death.

The trouble is generally at its most prevalent during early spring or summer when the cattle first go to graze lush leys or pastures, and the orthodox explanation is that an excessive ingestion of green food, particularly clover, is the cause. But all curative and preventative measures which have worked on this assumption have so far failed.

Though clover is an important factor, it is I believe, a secondary factor. It is not necessary for the cow to overeat to become blown. The danger is from the production of gases in the stomach and not from gorging. A cow will normally stop eating when her stomach is full. I have investigated internally many animals which have died from this trouble, and find that in practically every case there has been some undigested stale concentrate food present in the stomach; and though only a minute quantity, it has been sufficient, in combination with the clover, to start fermentation and the rapid production of gases. Most of the blown victims I have examined have been comparatively heavy milkers, consuming large quantities of production ration—unnatural food which is not only difficult to digest but lacks the vitamins and minerals which aid digestion. It has been found that the production ration is rarely completely digested until a long spell of spring grazing has provided the necessary digestive tone to enable it to clear up arrears in the stomach. The result is that during the early part of the summer, while undigested food still remains in the system, the risk of blown is great. As the summer advances, the risk becomes progressively less, not because the cow eats less clover or eats less quickly, but because the accumulations of the winter have been disposed of, and nothing remains to set up fermentation. Later in the summer and early in the autumn the danger increases again as the concentrated production ration is increased and digestion becomes more difficult.

PREVENTION

If, before the cow is put to grass, the stomach is completely emptied of stale food, there will be nothing to cause fermentation. Fast the cows for twenty-four hours, especially if there is a known tendency to blowing, and if you can get hold of some charcoal, in pieces about the size of a sixpence, or in tablet form, give four to six pieces to each animal.

213

Charcoal is a wonderful thing for absorbing stomach gases and preventing fermentation.

The long-term prevention, which I have found to have a most remarkable effect in eliminating blowing in my own herd, is to see that all the pastures contain a high proportion of herbs and deep-rooting grasses. Late flowering or broad red clovers should be kept to a minimum, not more than a total of 3 lb. per acre, where blowing is feared. The herbal ley has a remarkable effect in providing the minerals essential to efficient digestion, and also the coarser grazing which suits the stomach of the cow. Divide the leys into paddocks and graze the cows continuously at the rate of ten or twelve to the acre rather than 'on and off'.

TREATMENT

When a cow becomes blown the immediate treatment, after confining her without food, is to give a pint of linseed oil and, if you have them, four charcoal tablets, repeating them every half-hour until the trouble has gone. Keep the animal on the move to assist the movement of gas and to prevent her from lying down.

Where the distension of the stomach is causing obvious discomfort and appears likely to increase, the stomach should at once be pierced with a trocar and canula or, if this instrument is not available, an ordinary pen-knife. The point at which to pierce should be the highest point of the distended stomach, midway between the last rib and the hipbone—approximately a hand-span from each to the highest point of distension. Jab the knife or instrument sharply in to its full extent and move it about to ease the passage of gas.

Another means of getting gases to move is to make a twisted rope of hay or straw and put it as far as possible down the back of the cow's mouth. Some of her own dung thrust into the cow's mouth will encourage her to chew in an attempt to be rid of it, and this, in addition to the rope down the throat, will encourage the escape of gases. Additionally, insert a rubber tube—the thin milk tube of a milking machine is ideal—into the anus as far as possible and keep this moving to assist the escape of gas and dung from the rear end.

Once an animal has been blown she must have at least a twenty-four-hour fast before she is put to grass again. A large quantity of charcoal in some form will help to clear up remaining gases and fermenting foods during the fast.

OTHER DISEASES

MILK FEVER

Because Jersey cattle appear to be particularly prone to milk fever I have, perforce, been compelled to give much thought and experiment to this trouble.

Milk fever, or parturient apoplexy, though not strictly a fever, for there is rarely a high temperature, is commonly known as 'drop after calving.' The symptoms are a restlessness, at any time from a few hours after calving up to four weeks or so after calving, in which the cow starts by raising first one hind leg and then the other in a paddling fashion and eventually collapses. She lies down and repeatedly turns her head back to her ribs. As the condition develops she will throw her head and the whole of her body back to the ground and may reach the stage of a coma, when, if not attended to, she will die.

Perhaps more than any other disease it is the obvious result of over-exploitation of the cow. It is rarely found in poor milking cows and beef cattle, being confined almost entirely to dairy breeds and the heavier milking animals of those breeds. Further support of this theory is the fact that heifers never succumb to milk fever, and it is not until the cow has suffered two or three lactations of exploitation that she suffers. The third calving is usually the earliest time for milk fever.

It is caused by the strain on the system of the double stimulus of parturition and high-protein feeding on the flow of milk. With a heavy milking cow the stimulus of calving on the flow of milk is already great. To add the additional stimulus of high feeding is too much for the cow, the flush of milk is so sudden, and drains the blood-stream and the ductless glands of all the requirements of milk production—various minerals, calcium and hormones, that the rest of the body almost ceases to function and the cow collapses.

PREVENTION

Knowing that the cause is over-stimulation of the milk secretion, the prevention is simple and obvious—to reduce in all cases and to cut out completely, in cows known to have a tendency to milk fever, all foods likely to stimulate the flow of milk two weeks before calving. Feed in the ration during pregnancy a mineral-rich supplement which will build up the mineral reserves of the blood-stream and the supply of hormones, and in general bring the whole metabolism of the body to a high pitch of efficiency. The danger in high feeding is not so much the overfeeding of the animal as the inefficiency of the cow's metabolism to cope with the diet. A diet rich in minerals and plant hormones is known to be beneficial to the animal metabolism. This may be achieved by the use of seaweed on the land and in the diet. Channel Island cattle are particularly prone to milk fever away from the Channel Islands, and the obvious explanation is the change from a soil heavily dressed with seaweed, from which the cow derives the requirements of a highly efficient metabolism (this, I think, also explains the higher fat and solids content of milk in the Channel Islands), to soils which never get even as much as a smell of the sea, and in most cases previous little organic matter of any kind.

In addition to the use of seaweed, wherever possible, organic manuring and the use of deep-rooting herbs in the pastures will contribute greatly to improved metabolism and the prevention of milk fever.

TREATMENT

Having fed the cow to the point of milk fever, or having bought one just after someone else has 'steamed-up' and she goes down with milk fever, it is too late to be certain that seaweed powder will act quickly enough, though there is no doubt it will help. So milk out the udder and inflate it with the apparatus which you should have had in readiness beforehand and which is available from veterinary equipment suppliers.

The equipment consists of a teat syphon and filter chamber which filters the air which is blown through it into each quarter through the teat after the udder has been thoroughly washed and milked out. The effect of this inflation of the udder is to prevent any further flow of milk into the udder and stop the drain of hormones and minerals from the blood-stream to the udder. This enables the cow's system to adjust itself slowly to the demands which heavy milk production are putting upon it. The cow should also have a dose of two tablespoonfuls of seaweed powder in molasses and warm water (two tablespoonfuls of molasses), every three hours, until she is up and walking about again. Into this mixture should be added four leaf-plasma tablets each time, to supply the vital tonic elements of grasses and herbs without the protein stimulant.

It is essential that the cow be kept propped up in the normal sitting position with bales of straw. On no account allow her to stretch out on her side. Then, if she appears to be slowly improving, don't rush her to get up. She may, and quite understandably too, need a few hours' rest.

Grass Tetany is a more recent and more acute form of milk fever, and though it has been given a new name it has all the same symptoms and causes as milk fever, i.e. over-stimulation of milk secretion by the excessive protein of a rich clover ley, especially on top of the use of high-protein cattle cake. But because it is far quicker in its action, and results in death often before there has been an opportunity to treat the cow, it has been regarded as a separate disease. It may, however, be prevented in exactly the same way as milk fever, and the treatment is the same, should you be fortunate enough to catch the cow while she is still alive.

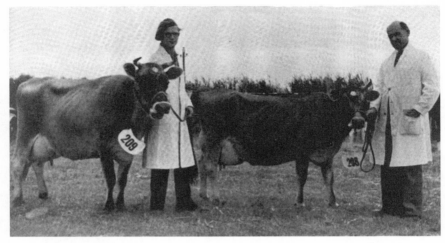

21a. Polden Dolly Daydream (left), winner of Royal Cornwall Show Milk and Butter Trials (see page 168) and Whitehall Roselaird, winner of many prizes and yielded 1,000 gallons with her first calf on home-grown food.

21b. Goosegreen senior stock bull, Top Sergente, at 8 years old, leads the Grand Parade of Jerseys as first-prize winner—Dorchester Show 1949 (See Plate 20b).

22. A convenient way of handling cattle, also adaptable as a service crate, used at Goosegreen Farm.

CHAPTER TWENTY-TWO

Observations on the Behaviour of Cows
With Some Possible Explanations

Certain cows almost cease production for twelve or twenty-four hours during the three-weekly heat period, either refusing to give down their milk or being incapable. Other cows show no change in the flow of milk and some even show a slight increase. The relationship between glandular secretions of hormones and milk production seems to control this. Some cows which have an inadequate hormone secretion call upon all available resources to raise the quantity of hormones required for the heat period, with the result that there is an inadequate secretion in the udder to keep the milk flowing. The cow therefore holds the milk until activity in the uterus and vagina slows down. I have found that whereas at such a time a cow of this type is unable or unwilling to give milk to the inanimate milking machine, she will respond to the human hand, thus demonstrating the stimulating effect of 'flesh to flesh' contact on the flow of hormones in the udder.

May it not be that the lack of emotional sensation which the cow feels in the mechanical milking process is one cause of increasing udder troubles, linked with the growing practice of disallowing the cow any emotional stimulus from the suckling of her calf (the practice in large herds being to take the calf away at birth)?

Cows which increase in yield at the time of oestrum do so by the over-production of hormones to all the organs that are associated with the process of reproduction. Hormones stimulate milk flow and a flush of hormones to the udder, brought on by the excitement of oestrum, causes a flush of milk.

It seems, then, that the effect of the heat period on the milk yield of a cow depends on the adequacy of glandular or endocrine secretions. If the cow has an ample functioning of the endocrines she will rise in yield; if her endocrines are not functioning properly she will draw from the udder for the effort of oestrum, and a fall in yield will result.

A cow with a balanced secretion of hormones will come on heat without affecting the milk yield.

PERIOD OF LACTATION AND THE STRAIN OF FERTILIZATION

A cow which is yielding heavily will sometimes show no oestrum until she is past the peak of her production, or, if she does come on heat, she will give one of four indications that hormone activity is not adequate to the two functions of high milk yield and fertilization.

1. She will fall markedly in yield for the period of the oestrum.

2. She will cease production altogether and show great difficulty in regaining output.

3. She will go wrong in one or more quarters, or

4. A combination of the first three.

If she is effectively fertilized while showing any one of these conditions the chances are that she will either abort or go seriously wrong in the udder before pregnancy is completed. Or she will have a weakly calf which will exhibit tendencies to difficult breeding or udder trouble in later life, if indeed it survives to maturity.

High yielders are therefore best kept empty until they are declining in yield.

SEASONAL INFLUENCES ON THE COW'S ABILITY TO RETAIN HER CALF IN UTERUS

Sarkies Dream—born 27th June 1937
> 1st calf 1st August 1939
> 2nd calf 17th August 1940
> 3rd calf September 1941
> 4th calf August 1942
> 5th calf 22nd July 1943, died at birth
> 6th calf 31st August 1944, aborted
> 7th calf February 1946, alive

Variety— born 16th July 1940
       1st calf 17th February 1943
   Slipped 2nd calf 5th July 1944
   "   3rd calf April 1945
   "   4th calf March 1946

April was like midsummer in 1945 and may have had the seasonal influences of July and August.

As far as Sarkies Dream is concerned, it seems that she has some difficulty in carrying a calf through the summer months. Twice in successive summers she has been found with her udder and the lower half of her body immersed in a stream or water ditch, indicating the possible excess of heat in the udder and sexual organs. An exaggeration of this condition in thundery weather may cause the cow to reject the calf from the uterus and thus reduce the temperature in the region of the uterus.

The same explanation may easily apply to Variety, July 1944 and April 1945 being much alike in weather.

I have found that the summer months show the highest incidence of abortions. This may, of course, be explainable by the higher percentage of autumn calvers aborting at seven months (which is the most common stage), thus falling in the summer.

Clematis, who has a habit of calving twins, is one of the cows who also increases her milk yield during the heat period. She also has the habit of following almost any human that may enter the field, trailing at heel like a dog. This desire to have human contact may have a sexual significance; a strong development of the instinct which makes a herd of cows investigate any strange intrusion to the field in which they may be grazing, i.e. the advent of a calf, a bull, or a strange dog; all, no doubt, having some emotional stimulus on the sexual instincts of maternity (protection of young or desire to procreate the species, etc.).

FERTILIZATION AND ITS EFFECT ON THE UDDER OF
    Variety—AND OTHERS

It has been my observation that clots in the milk, in one or more quarters, are a frequent aftermath of fertilization of a cow which is not adequate to the task of pregnancy. The system at the time of nidation is no longer able to perform satisfactorily the two functions of milk secretion and foetus nutrition simultaneously. Consequently, if nidation is successful, the udder often suffers.

Variety, previously mentioned in connection with frequent abortion, was served for her fifth calf on 15th July 1946. On 3rd August 1946 she gave clotted milk in watery substance in the near front quarter. At this time she had been allowed to diminish in yield as low as one gallon daily before being served. It is clear, then, that in the case of this cow she is not able to give milk and become pregnant at the same time without ill consequence to her health.

The above notes record typical examples of many observations bearing on my theory that diseases of cows such as mastitis, abortion, sterility, are not primarily caused by bacteria. They point to faulty endocrine functions as a more potent cause, resulting from unnatural methods of management and going right back to inadequate nutrition of soil, crops, and animals.

I am convinced that this line of action will be far more effective in the elimination of animal disease than the old-fashioned germicidal warfare.

CHAPTER TWENTY-THREE

The Dread Disease—Abortion

Abortion, or the premature expulsion of the foetus by a pregnant animal, may be accidental; that is, caused by violent injury, such as a blow from another animal, or it may be due to structural malformation, or, what is perhaps the most common form, that which is due to the toxic condition of the animal system which makes it not only impossible, but inadvisable for the animal to carry the pregnancy to full term. Associated with the last condition, and often a cause alone, may be the rearing and maintenance of the animal during the whole or part of its lifetime on land which is seriously inadequate in the requirements of a healthy pregnancy, or in the prerequisites of proper growth and development of the breeding female.

It is not possible here to deal more than briefly with the accidental, and the fundamental, causes of premature parturition or unhealthy pregnancy. The first can only be avoided by careful measures for prevention, such as the provision of ample yarding or other accommodation for pregnant animals, gentle handling and, above all, with cattle, the use of a dog in driving or herding should be absolutely forbidden. With the latter cause, which I have called fundamental, i.e. caused by soil or atmospheric deficiencies or abnormality, it is choice of farm, and the methods of soil management and cropping—matters referred to elsewhere—that are of more importance than the actual treatment of the animal. Farms in extremely low-lying and excessively humid areas are not conducive to completely and continuously trouble-free breeding. Though it may be possible to bring the animals to a high state of health, there will be periods when pregnancy and parturition abnormalities occur, and though they are temporarily inconvenient and upsetting to the planning of the farm programme, as well as the mental calm of the farmer, they have no serious or permanent effect on the ability of the animals for future breeding.

The cause which is most common, most serious in its results if not properly tackled, and yet the simplest to avoid and cure on the farm organically managed, is that which results from the toxic condition of the animal system. The orthodox veterinary profession, and indeed the whole of orthodox agricultural science, calls this 'contagious' abortion, and blames the bacillus which was discovered by Dr. Bang—*Brucella abortus* or *bacterium abortum,* which is generally found in the catarrhal discharges and the blood-stream of animals aborting for reasons of toxaemia (the condition in which accumulations of poisons in the form of catarrh are present in the system).

Nature has good purpose in all her processes, and the pro-cess of abortion is one of them. The bacteria which the scientist isolates and blames for causing the condition, merely arises out of the condition as an essential part of the curative process. As explained in my introduction to the subject of disease, the bacteria are entirely benevolent and engaged in the work of consuming the toxic accumulations and assisting their discharge from the body. The act of abortion, or expulsion of the foetus, is a part of the natural elimination of toxins from the overloaded system, and as such is altogether beneficial to the ultimate health of the animal. The loss of the calf, or foal, or lamb, or kid, should not be regarded as a disaster, but as a life-saver for the dam, which at best would otherwise become permanently sterile and incapable of further useful existence on the farm. As it is, with orthodox treatment she will probably become at least temporarily sterile, and if the bad feeding which caused the toxaemia continues, permanent sterility, or other serious toxic condition, is almost certain.

But with enlightened management and organic treatment, the act of abortion becomes a healing process in the life of the animal whose subsequent health and productive ability will be wonderfully benefited as a result.

Symptoms. Taking the example of a cow (in which abortion is more common than in other animals due to the more exploitive methods of management), where the normal calving date of the animal is known, it is a simple matter to anticipate a threatened abortion. Approaching the third, fifth or seventh month of pregnancy, though it does also occur at other periods, a slight discharge may be noticed from the vulva, and the vulva will become relaxed and bright pink in colour. If the animal is dry the udder may or may not show signs of freshening, depending on the milking capacity of the cow and the length of time she has been dry. If she is in milk, some abnormality will be noticed in the milk, such as thickening, discolouration or clotting. With a cow in milk, the first symptom is often the appearance of clots in the milk and the change to a sticky texture in the milk, and if this is associated with some reddening and slackening of the vulva, abortion is almost certain. If there is no change in the vulva, and the cow is immediately put under treatment, it may be possible to get away with mere temporary udder trouble, but once a distinct relaxation of the vulva is plainly evident, only the most skilful treatment will avoid abortion.

If careful note has been made of the sexual cycle, or if, with a cow accustomed to regular heat periods, a calculation of the heat periods had the cow not become pregnant, it will be found that abortion usually takes place, or seriously threatens, or udder trouble is evident, at the time the cow would have been on heat had she not been in calf. This indicates the close relationship between all the organs of reproduction, the udder, the uterus, the ovaries, the vulva, and the fact that they are all interdependent and jointly responsible for the success or otherwise of the pregnancy. The time of sexual crisis, in the female, is the heat period. It is at this time that the greatest strain is present, and whether or not the animal is pregnant the cycle continues with its phases of 'heat and cool', the heat period being the occasion of trouble if the system is not equal to the task in hand. In less toxic conditions, udder trouble is the worst that happens in these periods of the sexual cycle; in worse conditions abortion takes place, and in the most toxic cases both udder trouble and abortion are simultaneous or closely following one another. Sterility is the almost certain consequence of the abortion which is also accompanied by udder trouble, as the cow is obviously in so toxic a state that drastic cleansing of the whole system is called for before the animal can be capable of performing any healthy function. Even in the milder cases of abortion, temporary sterility is frequent because, of course, the cow cannot be expected to carry a calf in a uterus that continues the catarrhal discharges which caused the abortion.

TREATMENT BEFORE ABORTION

Prevention is rarely possible once the obvious symptoms are observed. But, provided organic methods are the rule on the farm and the herdsman is a master of his work and able to detect the slightest abnormality in his cattle—the best herdsmen often have an uncanny ability to sense impending abnormalities—it is possible to commence treatment which will avert an actual abortion. It is not possible, however, in case of animals that have been running with the bull and no service date is known, to be sure whether the signs are those of abortion or normal calving, except from the udder. If the animal appears to be about to calve without making much of an udder, then it is likely to be a premature calving.

As with all toxic conditions, fasting is the immediate necessity. After the first twenty-four hours without food (as it may encourage expulsion of the foetus, it is not possible to give the usual enema), some form of gentle herbal purgative should be given. The liquid from twelve senna pods soaked overnight in two pints of warm water should be given as a drench on the morning and night of the second day of the fast, and repeated on the third day.

As abortion is basically a catarrhal condition, the best possible cleanser is garlic in some form. If garlic grows wild on the farm, then whole plants should be gathered and fed at the rate of four whole plants daily for two weeks, but commencing with one only on the first day, increasing by one each day. If no wild garlic is available, four flaked cloves may be fed morning and night, similarly commencing with one only the first morning and increasing to a daily ration of four cloves morning and night. If the cow will not readily take the flaked garlic cloves, or even the whole garlic plants (which is unlikely as her system will be demanding it), it may be chopped and mixed with a little kale or silage or other appetizing food and a little molasses, or made into a ball with bran.

Failing either garlic plant or root, the prepared tablets of whole crushed and compressed garlic may be used, giving six tablets in a little water morning and night. The tablets need not dissolve. The water is merely to assist passage of the tablets to the stomach, where they will dissolve and achieve digestion slowly, at the same time penetrating the whole system and purifying the unclean places.

During the fast the animal should be kept in and allowed access to ample clean water, which should preferably not be from a tap. Spring, stream, or even well water is preferable for an animal in normal health, and even more so for a sick animal, as it contains vital elements not present in the chlorinated dead water of the Rural District Council.

The fast should be continued for a week or until signs of impending abortion are passed. At the end of a week, if there is no worsening of the condition, molasses should be fed, commencing with a pint on the first day, increasing by one pint daily, to two pints morning and night. This should be given as a drench, diluted in warm water to a consistency which makes it capable of being poured from a bottle. The genuine *cane* molasses should be used.

If, during the second week, the animal appears to be happy and normal, organically grown green food may be introduced in small quantities, gradually increasing to normal rations of 20 or 30 lb. of good kale, and at the end of the second week a small bran mash—3 to 4 lb. of bran—may be given with added molasses, and then organically-grown cereals introduced. If, in the second week, the animal still appears abnormal the fast should continue another week. In any case, the garlic should continue daily till calving, as a safeguard and insurance of healthy calving.

TREATMENT AFTER ABORTION

If, in spite of all preventive efforts, the animal aborts, or if, as so often happens, abortion has taken place without the warnings having been observed, then the only treatment is one that takes advantage of the natural cleansing process which has been commenced, to take the opportunity of getting the animal back to a condition of normal health in which she may enjoy healthy pregnancy in the future.

Immediate action for the cow should be to provide, if pos-sible, the natural stimulus of a calf. If a young calf is available, this should be put to suckle the cow at once. This will help to stimulate the normal hormone secretions which have a cleansing effect on the uterus and which are responsible for milk flow and udder health. The calf should be left with the cow day and night and allowed to suckle at will. If the cow does not take readily to the calf she must be trained by holding, three times a day, until the calf may be left to help itself. The suckling calf is by far the best treatment for any abnormal calving or udder trouble, calling forth the endocrine secretions of the ductless glands—called hormones—which play a major part in the maintenance of health in the organs of reproduction and milk production, and adjusts the abnormalities which artificial treatment may have caused.

Thereafter, the cow should be given the two-weeks' treatment for the prevention of abortion but with daily enemas, both rectal and vaginal, using four gallons of warm water in which eight crushed garlic tablets have been dissolved. If possible, the last half-gallon of water containing garlic should in each case be retained in the intestine and vagina.

Additionally, throughout the two weeks, a daily dose of raspberry-leaf tea, or a blend of birth herbs, such as raspberry leaves, motherwort, and linseed, should be given. Four to five ounces of mixed dried birth herbs or, failing a mixture of these herbs, dried raspberry leaves brewed in a gallon of water, will make four two-pint drenches, to be given morning and night. If raspberry leaves are available on the farm, a bucketful of fresh leaves may be soaked in water, boiled, and the liquid given in two-pint drenches morning and night.

This treatment should be repeated monthly three times, and if effective service does not result after the second fasting period, monthly until service is effective.

In such serious cases the fast should be for two weeks before the week of introducing green food and, later, cereals.

It may be that the cow shows signs of milking well in spite of aborting, in which case drastic fasting may be delayed for a couple of months. But a week's fast, with garlic and birth herbs, should in any case be given as soon as possible after the abortion and while the cow is suckling a calf, and cereal feeding should be withheld as long as possible—at least two weeks—with the exception of bran mash with molasses, in which the dried raspberry leaves may be given instead of as a liquid drench.

Fasting for a week does not permanently affect milk yield where the cow's health calls for a fast. Indeed, it will benefit subsequent milk yield, and the cow will usually recover at least the yield of the pre-fasting period or, even more, as a result of the benefit to general health.

Conclusion

Were it not that it is only in comparatively recent years that it has become possible to prepare the soil satisfactorily on a commercial basis without the plough, one might be amazed at the apparent slowness of farmers to dispense with this tool. But it is only with the development of the tractor, and the heavy disc harrow which could not be drawn by horses, that it has become possible to incorporate organic matter and green crops effectively into surface soil which has lost its friability.

The methods described in this book work well on my land, and I am convinced they apply to any type of soil, in any part of the world. They are the methods practised by nature in any part of the world. They are the methods practised by nature on all ranges of soil, from the thinnest shale to the deepest loam. Even on a rock, nature enables plants to grow, so long as the seed is provided with a light covering of organic matter to hold the moisture, gather nutrients from the air, and supply the products of decay. If nature can grow a vigorous and healthy plant on a *rock*, as any student of the countryside may see for himself, then there is no excuse for the farmer or gardener, with *soil* at his disposal, to have to resort to artificial methods of crop production.

This is clearly the clue to our downfall as husbandmen. We have had the audacity to assume that we know better than God. We have believed we could improve on the ways of nature and we find ourselves under the threat of famine, in spite of so-called scientific genius. God in His goodness has provided the means to abundance; we in our greed and arrogance have perverted and destroyed. The only way we can repair the harm we have done is to give nature a chance to work in her own way and, as far as we must interfere by way of farming and gardening, let it be in imitation of nature rather than in battle against nature.

There is one further provision which is essential to complete the cycle of fertility and it is an urgent and imperative one if Britain is to evade eventual starvation. That is the return to the soil—properly composted, to avoid unpleasantness—of all sewage sludge and organic town refuse. I will not elaborate on this matter, though it is fundamen-

Notes on Goosegreen Farm

Goosegreen Farm has 180 acres all in cultivation except 11 acres of apple orchards and about 10 acres of hill and rough grazing.

The farmstead is at an elevation of only 40 feet above sea-level and the fields slope up to the small Polden Hills. The soil is red marl formerly extremely heavy and difficult to work as may be seen from the fields furthest from the house that have not had the same benefit from organic methods—particularly compost—i.e. Soggers, Righton's Grave.

The stock consists of approximately 80–90 head of pedigree Jersey cattle, including a number that have been taken in for treatment, a horse and poultry. All animals are normally fed on the produce of the farm which means we carry cattle at the rate of more than one to each two acres of cropped land, in addition to other livestock.

BUILDINGS

When we first came to this farm in February, 1941, it was in a derelict state and nothing has been done to the buildings except essential repairs and the installation of a milking parlour and dairy. Much therefore still needs to be done. But capital has been extremely limited and we were reduced to scratch by the ravages of disease in the early years. Everything, therefore, has to be done out of income. Hence the strictest economy on non-productive expenditure.

Goosegreen is consequently a hard-working farm, without any frills. It is *not* a model farm, though we think our methods with the land and livestock might constitute a practical model of farming that can maintain health in crops and stock and at the same time yield profitably.

Mechanization has been very limited and only on a scale accessible to the smallest farmer—a tractor, a milking machine, an ex-Army lorry, disc harrows and light tooth harrows, reaper and binder are the essentials.

We hope we are demonstrating that successful organic farming does not require large expenditure of either money or labour.

THE HERD

The pedigree Jersey herd was founded eight years ago after costing two Jerseys against the Shorthorns and Friesians taken over with the farm. Only three times have we paid more than £90 for an animal and then for special breeding purposes. Some of the cows were bought for £5 to £15 as incurable. By treatment and breeding, we have built up a profitable herd from animals of low-priced origin.

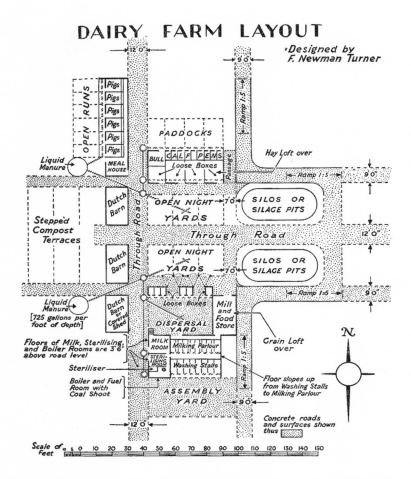

DAIRY FARM LAYOUT

Designed by F. Newman Turner

The plan of dairy farm buildings is designed for the most economical utilization of space, time and labour. The buildings are grouped around the yards into which goes all the food and out of which comes the farmyard manure. Thus, the silos or pits for silage and the Dutch barns for hay and straw are immediately adjoining the yards so that silage may be fed directly to the yards as well as straw for bedding. A concrete road runs right through the yards to carry silage in to the cows and manure out to the compost terraces (which are stepped for ease of loading and turning if necessary). The liquid manure tanks adjoin the compost terraces so that liquid manure may be sprayed over surplus straw (from the Dutch barns) on the compost terraces.

The passage of the cows is from the night-yards down the north to south through-road, to the assembly yards. From there they pass to the washing stalls thence to be milked in the milking stalls and out to the dispersal yard. From the dispersal yard, gates are arranged so that access may be allowed to each yard separately. Ramps surround the silage pits and lofted buildings for ease of loading, both into the silage pits and the lofts above the food store and loose boxes. The roadway through the silage pits is at ground level for ease of emptying the silage pits.

236

Resources

Below are updated contact points mentioned by N. Turner that are still in existence today. The avid student will no doubt turn up additional sources.

The Soil Association, South Plaza, Marlborough Street, Bristol BS1 3NX, United Kingdom, phone 0117-314-5000, website *www.soilassociation.org.*

Cotswold Seed Ltd. [Herbal Ley Seed Distributor], Cotswold Business Village, Moreton-in-Marsh, Gloucestershire GL56 0JQ, United Kingdom, website *www.cotswoldseeds.co.uk/ herballeys.htm.*

ANIMAL HEALTH ASSOCIATIONS

United States Animal Health Association, P.O. Box 8805, St Joseph, Missouri 64508, phone 816-671-1144, website *www. usaha.org.*

Institute for Animal Health, Compton Laboratory, Compton, Newbury, Berks RG20 7NN, United Kingdom, website *www. iah.bbsrc.ac.uk.*

New Zealand Association for Animal Health and Crop Protection, P.O. Box 5069, Wellington, New Zealand, website *www1.agcarm.co.nz.*

Animal Health Alliance Ltd., Level 2, AMP Building, 1 Hobart Place, Canberra, ACT 2601, Australia, website *www. animalhealthalliance.org.au.*

DEXTER CATTLE SOCIETIES

American Dexter Cattle Association, 4150 Merino Avenue, Watertown, Minnesota 55388, phone 952-215-2206, website *www.dextercattle.org.*

The Dexter Cattle Society, 1st Floor, RASE Offices, Stoneleigh Park, Warks CV8 2LZ, United Kingdom, phone 0247-669-2300, website *www. dextercattle.co.uk.*

Dexter Cattle Society New Zealand, 92A Takanini-Clevedon Road, Ardmore, RD 2, Papakura, Aukland, New Zealand, website *www.dexter-cattle.co.nz.*

Dexters—Beefy Little Milkers, ABRI—University of New England, Armidale, NSW 2351, Australia, website *dexter.une. edu.au.*

Estimating Quantities of Silage, Hay, Straw, Roots and Compost, in Stacks and Heaps

1. (a) If rectangular, multiply length by breadth by height.
   (b) If circular, multiply circumference by itself and by .08 and then by height.
   (c) If prism, multiply length by breadth at base and then by half the height.
   (d) If cone, multiply circumference at base by itself and by .08 and then by one-third the perpendicular height.

2. Add (a) and (c) or (b) and (d) together: the result will be contents in cubic feet if measurements taken in feet.

3. Reduce to cubic yards by dividing by 27.

4. Reduce to tons by dividing by one of the following numbers according to the shape and condition of the stack:

	Number of Cubic Yards Per Ton	
Hay Weights	Rectangular	Round
If not settled	12	13
If compact	8	9

Straw	Number of Cubic Yards Per Ton
	Wheat 18–20, Oats 20–23, Barley 20–23

Roots	
	Weight Per Cubic Foot in Clamp
	Turnips 33 lb., Mangolds 35 lb., Carrots 31 lb., Swedes 34 lb., Potatoes 42 lb., Parsnips 31 lb.

Compost. One cubic yard of compost weighs 12 to 16 cwt., or one ton of compost bulks $1\frac{1}{4}$ to $1\frac{3}{8}$ cubic yards, when mature.

Silos. A silo 15 feet diameter and 30 feet high (5,300 cubic feet) holds 100 tons of silage, the yield of 6 acres of maize, 10 acres of oats and vetches, 13 acres of clover ley, 20 acres meadow grass, 12 acres sainfoin or lucerne: one cut in each case.

A silo 12 feet diameter and 24 feet high has half the above capacity.

Pit Silage. One cubic yard of finished silage weighs approximately one ton.

Recommended Reading

The following titles were suggested for further study by the author. Many are available in reproduction editions or from rare book dealers.

RECOMMENDED READING

An Agricultural Testament, Sir Albert Howard (Oxford University Press).

Farming and Gardening for Health or Disease, Sir Albert Howard (Faber & Faber Limited).

Problems in Tree Nutrition, M. C. Rayner and W. Neilson-Jones (Faber & Faber Limited).

The Earth's Green Carpet, Louise E. Howard (Faber & Faber Limited).

The Living Soil, Eve Balfour (Faber & Faber Limited).

Nutrition and Physical Degeneration, Weston A. Price.

Ploughman's Folly, E. H. Faulkner (Michael Joseph Limited).

The Green Leaf, Louise E. Howard (Howard Foundation).

Soil Fertility and Sewage, J. P. J. van Vuren (Faber & Faber Limited).

Soil Conditions and Plant Growth, Sir E. John Russell (Longmans, Green & Company Limited).

Gardening with Compost, F. C. King (Faber & Faber Limited).

Use Our Sewage and Refuse, Dr. H. Martin-Leake (Howard Foundation).

Municipal Composting, L. P. Brunt (Supplement to above).

Humus and the Farmer, Friend Sykes (Faber & Faber Limited).

Reconstruction by Way of the Soil, G. T. Wrench (Faber & Faber Limited).

The Clifton Park System of Farming, Robert H. Elliot (Faber & Faber Limited).

Cleanliness and Godliness, Reginald Reynolds (Allen & Unwin Limited).

Organic Husbandry—A Symposium, J. S. Blackburn.

Index

Also by Newman Turner

Herdsmanship
by Newman Turner

In this book, Turner explains that livestock illness is a result of bad farming practices and that real livestock health begins with true natural farming disciplines such as composting, biodiverse pastures with deep-rooted forages and herbs, and sub-soiling, as well as the avoidance of supposed panaceas that ignore or marginalize these fundamentals such as vaccines, pesticides, antibiotics and artificial fertilizers. He teaches that the cornerstones of profitability are rooted in herd health, which in turn is rooted in: soil fertility and animal nutrition, cattle breeding for better feed efficiency, and cattle breeding for longevity. Longevity, he holds, is the most critical factor for success in livestock breeding and production. *Softcover, 272 pages. ISBN 978-1-601730-10-7*

Fertility Pastures
by Newman Turner

In *Fertility Pastures*, Turner details his methods of intensive pasture-based production of beef and dairy cows in a practical guide to profitable, labor-saving livestock production. He developed a system of complex "herbal ley mixtures," or blends of pasture grasses and herbs, with each ingredient chosen to perform an essential function in providing a specific nutrient to the animal or enhancing the fertility of the soil. He explains his methods of cultivation, seeding and management. There are also chapters on year-round grazing, making silage for self-feeding, protein from forage crops, and pastures for pigs and poultry. He also details the roles individual herbs play in the prevention and treatment of disease. *Softcover, 224 pages. ISBN 978-1-601730-11-4*

Cure Your Own Cattle
by Newman Turner

In this booklet, Newman Turner sought to "bring within the reach of the farmer a solution to his disease problems in a way in which drug and chemical treatments have never before achieved." He relied on his lifetime of observing animals and herbs in their natural environment to guide him in his experiments. The end result is his proclamation that freedom from animal diseases may be attained by the proper utilization of nature's provisions. While the subject of natural veterinary care has grown and matured, Turner's clear and simple systems and advice remind farmers of the true fundamentals that consistently work. *Softcover, 96 pages. ISBN 978-1-601730-08-4*

To order call 1-800-355-5313
or order online at *www.acresusa.com*